ONE MIND, COMMON TO ALL

THE MACMILLAN COMPANY
NEW YORK · CHICAGO
DALLAS · ATLANTA · SAN FRANCISCO
LONDON · MANILA

BRETT-MACMILLAN LTD.
TORONTO

ONE MIND,
COMMON TO ALL

by

Earl D. Bond, M.D.

PAST-PRESIDENT, AMERICAN PSYCHIATRIC ASSOCIATION. FROM THE INSTITUTE OF THE PENNSYLVANIA HOSPITAL

There is one mind common to all individual men. Every man is an inlet to the same, and to all of the same.

RALPH WALDO EMERSON

THE MACMILLAN COMPANY
New York, 1958

616.89
B 711

Acknowledgments

I thank Mr. Don Rose, of the Philadelphia Bulletin, and Mr. Henry Van Swearingen, of The Macmillan Company, for encouragement and criticism.

FOREWORD

THE ADVENT of a book by Doctor Earl D. Bond is a noteworthy event; the sad thing is that there is not a whole host of them. One of American psychiatry's senior statesmen and by now the most senior of the American Psychiatric Association's ex-presidents, he not only has witnessed the evolution of the specialty but also has had a guiding hand in it.

Occupied continually with the problems of the emotionally distressed and the mentally ill since 1908, when he began as an assistant physician at McLean Hospital, in Waverley, Massachusetts, Doctor Bond obviously speaks with authority born of long experience. However, authority and seniority, important as they are, are the more minor of his attributes—for, in addition, he has exerted a beneficent and wholesome influence upon hundreds of men who learned their psychiatry under his aegis. At last count, several years ago, the heads of more than thirty teaching institutions had been educated under the mellow influence of Doctor Bond and his Institute. This writer counts himself fortunate to be one of that number.

One thing the neophyte learned (and he was educated rather than trained) in his early encounters with Doctor Bond was that calmness and equanimity were his watchwords. Whether one was resident or patient—and, not infrequently in the early stages, these roles were indistinguishable—to see him and talk to him was to emerge with the feeling that everything was certain to come out all right. One learned, too, that scientific knowledge did not necessarily have to be dispensed in atmospheres ponderous or bilious, but rather that wisdom and counsel could be accompanied by humor and compassion. This was a major revelation in those days, and it kept many young men in psychiatry who might otherwise have gone off to be orthopedists, obstetricians, or even acrobats.

In his address, kindly, and in his addresses, brief, his touch was light and gentle, but effective nonetheless. Whether he was discussing Doctor Kirkbride and his Hospital, or whether he was advising the exquisite and sweet-smelling young ladies of a fashionable Eastern college that they were beautifully educated but emotionally lopsided, he always spoke courteously and with the touch of a master. I recall that he advised this last group to hie themselves quickly to mental hospitals as soon as commencement was over.

Now, with nearly fifty years of experience and with the deep respect of all his colleagues, Doctor Bond writes about the things he learned from patients. Not only is the work urbane and scholarly, but of necessity, since it comes from his pen, it is presented in delightful fashion.

FRANCIS J. BRACELAND, M.D.
President (1956–57),
American Psychiatric Association

CONTENTS

To the Patients who have taught me

Chapter I

EDUCATION
OF A PSYCHIATRIST

LOVE AND HATE, courage and fear, are intermingled in all of us. Many fine men and women go about their work, their living, and their loving with unnecessary burdens of hate and unhappiness on their shoulders. Many, without knowing why, walk always in the shadow of fear and guilt, as real a shadow as overcasts a clouded mind in a mental hospital. Some who lead the way in science cannot find their way in social relationships. Men who manage the most complicated and delicate machines are clumsy and destructive in dealing with their fellow men. In general there is no difference, except in degree, between the symptoms of patients who have a definite illness of mind and the rest of us, including our leaders.

How much mental health is in our leaders, our congressmen, our advertisers, our candidates running for office, our patients in psychiatric hospitals? How much mental health is normal? What is normal, anyway? Where is the dividing line that leaves normal persons on one side and abnormal ones on the other?

When I entered the field of psychiatry nearly half a century ago, these questions did not worry me. It is difficult for me now to realize that I assumed that abnormal people were in psychiatric hospitals and normal people were outside. I never put this assumption into words; I never even formulated it in my mind. But it was there.

Now the matter is not so clean-cut. To mention just one side of my education, I have seen a surprising amount of normality in patients with severe mental diseases, in spite of overwhelming swings of mood in some and delusions and hallucinations in others.

But mental patients soon showed me that, in addition to a degree of normal thinking, they had much to teach about mental health—something unique, powerful, deep. They often exaggerated so as to make visible the mental forces that are concealed in most of us. They were honest as we cannot afford to be. Said one, "Something in my mind has not kept up with the rest of me—something made up of childish tangles of love and hate that have no rhyme or reason in a grown person." Also I learned that mental patients are often too logical or unselfish or emotional or sensitive for the world they live in. But so, in some degree and with infinite variety, are we all. The late Dr. Elmer E. Eyman, speaking of the psychotic patients he knew so well, said, "They are just like ourselves, only more so."

And patients with lesser mental disorder, those who have neuroses, can also teach, with less exaggeration but more finesse.

A way to increase and improve mental health is to stop, look, and listen to what these unhappy and upset people can tell us and teach us.

In the past quarter century I have met a great many normal and successful people who carried with them the usual one or two neurotic symptoms—and knew it. They have shown a courageous willingness to tell the truth about themselves in order to help themselves and in the hope of helping others. The changing ways and customs of our culture have made it possible for them to do so, for to be a little "off the beam" in one or two directions is no longer regarded as disgraceful or reprehensible. They also can be our teachers in the "proper study of mankind," which is the mind of man and the way it works or fails to work as it should and could.

Together these many people, from the least to the most disturbed, make up a great university faculty which could teach us much if we were willing to listen and learn. By turns desperate, intuitive, and calm, they plead for more reason and realism in the minds of us all. But realistic reasonableness is not a popular doctrine; to use it seems to some people a fate worse than death. At best it is an upsetting business, not very polite, frequently unpleasant. It reveals the underside of the stone as well as the shining surface. Often it calls for such old-fashioned commodities as courage to see one's own faults, confession, and repentance.

One side of my education as a psychiatrist was the finding of normality in patients with mild and severe mental diseases. A second side of that learning process was the observation of abnormality in people assumed to be in mental health—in everyday people carrying on the work of the world, in leaders in all aspects of our civilization.

An early experience was to leave a logical and cooperative patient to meet an unreasonable and confused relative. Were both the patient and the relative on the wrong side of the hospital entrance?

Then I filed away a minor incident for future reference. A quartet of singers and an accompanist had given a concert at the hospital where I was working and were thrown out of their carriage and injured on the hospital grounds. In the emergency, they were cared for by our doctors and nurses. In our mental hospital they proved to be so emotional and unreasonable that we were all relieved to see the last of them and get back to our usual patients, who were "mental cases" but more consistent and more predictable in their behavior.

I believe this episode marked a turning point in my professional and personal attitude toward patients and people. It came to mind again about thirty years ago, when my entire time and professional interest were devoted to the hospital treatment of acute and severe mental illness.

The hospital was on the north side of Market Street, in Philadelphia. On the south side, directly opposite, was a large hall known as the Arena, where a marathon dance was under way. A newspaper reporter invited me to watch the dancers with him. We saw "normal, sane, and sensible" citizens of Philadelphia staggering about in pairs, dead weary, holding each other up while a phonograph blared the same tune over and over. The dancers' feet were sore, their eyes bleary, and the stink of them filled the hall. Other "normal" people had paid money to watch the fantastic proceedings.

Soon I had seen more than enough and went back to the "abnormal" people across the street. One patient there was writing a book about an expedition to the North Pole, which was later published. Some were playing croquet or gardening; it was a pleasant day for outdoor occupations, which the "normals" in the Arena hadn't seemed to know or notice. Some of our mental patients were rehearsing a play; others were reading. There were a few whose rhythmic, repetitive motions reminded me of the dancers across the street, though the mental cases had more grace in their movements than the marathon dancers.

I was glad to feel more at home north of Market Street. There was much more sense to life in a mental hospital than there was to life as they were living it that day in the Arena. As the years went by, I saw clearly that the things which mental patients say and do make more and more sense, while the words and actions of ordinary people—much of the time—make less and less. In other words, all of us have *partly* normal minds.

A chance to confirm this statement came when the Pennsylvania Hospital opened an institute for outpatients and inpatients with the notion of "carrying what has been learned from mental patients to the most normal and gifted people we can find." This led to my working not only with people who had neuroses, but also with people who were too tired to work efficiently and with normal people who were in the grip of abnormal circumstance. Finally, it led to a study of people chosen for their normality and success.

I have said that our mental patients may be our teachers; but how may the lessons they teach be organized into a kind of curriculum? A new way, which I think has not been tried before, to use the teaching of this fabulous faculty is to imagine all the men and women of the United States on a downward sloping line, with the most normal at the top and the least normal at the bottom. The line would include you and me, our friends and our neighbors, "rich man, poor man, beggarman, thief, doctor, lawyer, merchant, chief," and also the patients in state mental hospitals.

Now look at this long line, and notice the large groups that appear upon it. Near the top is a place reserved for men and women in whom there is no flaw, no prejudice, no undue anxiety, no foolish behavior, no deviation in clear thinking. Would such people be rather hopelessly well balanced—rather dull? Are there many? One deep thinker has said that he could find only three completely "normal" persons in the world's history: "One was Socrates, Benjamin Franklin the second—and modesty forbids me to name the third."

Next to the paragons would stand a great throng of people who do the world's work and do it well. They do have what may be called fragments of neuroses, one or two nervous habits and symptoms which bother and handicap them. Some may be overconscientious or supersensitive; some have unnecessary fears or prejudices. But they are invaluable and interesting people because of their ability to get the better of their imperfections and to help and serve others.

Next comes a large group of those who have enough symptoms to be diagnosed as having neuroses. Something within them reduces their efficiency and happiness. Something diverts their full attention from the important things of the present to irrelevant things of the past, or to imaginary things of the future. But what amazing, wonderful, and talented people they are! They are creative artists, imaginative thinkers, adventurers, and inventors, capable of brilliant flashes of wisdom matched by moments of childish thinking and behavior. Their neuroses trouble or torment and, perhaps, inspire them.

In and out of neurotic states are the misers, tramps, fanatics, dictators, geniuses, ivory tower dwellers, alcoholics—the last three apt to move far up or down the line at any moment. A motley crew, indeed, but among them are those who have written the liveliest pages in human history.

Now come mental patients with acute illnesses, most of them profound depressions or transient states of confusion. Here the mind is either overpowered by one deep emotion or diseased by some temporary toxin. Most of the individuals who are in this category today will go far up the line tomorrow, while others will take their places.

Then we come to those who have severe, long-standing mental diseases, a most interesting and important set for our present purpose. A part of their minds works well and a part works poorly. The split, or separation, is what makes them sick and miserable. Their problems are familiar; they are everyday affairs in the minds of most men and women who do not get seriously upset or become dominated by them. And next week or next month some of these patients, not many, will make full recoveries and move far up the line.

It is tragic that an increasing group makes up the rest of the line, composed of men and women whose minds are nearly or totally useless because the brain tissues have been destroyed in old age or damaged by disease. In them failing memory is often a merciful blessing, because they cannot recall their depressing lives from day to day. They live, but they do not have the nervous apparatus to suffer much, and many of them live too long.

With brain damage still further increased, we come to zero in normal thinking and doing—the end of the line.

This, then, is the line-up of our common humanity, in which no two individuals ever born have been identical in thought and deed, as all are different in the pattern of their fingerprints. Yet the differences are less than the likenesses. The mind of every man is compounded of elements that are the heritage of his race. Emerson put it well when he wrote: "There is one mind

common to all individual men. Every man is an inlet to the
same and to all of the same." Tolstoy said wisely, "Every man
bears within himself the germs of every human quality, display-
ing all in turn." John Donne knew that "no man is an island,"
sufficient unto himself and unconcerned with the needs and
problems of others. "Ask not for whom the bell tolls; it tolls for
thee."

This means that within myself are the abilities, the defects,
the devices of the mental patient. Every time a neurosis or delusion appears in a community, my own mental health comes
into question; just as when riot or war comes to a village in
Indochina or on the Israel-Egypt frontier, it comes to my American town. And if I say that mental patients are unreasonable
and emotional, rationalizing their errors, projecting their sins
upon others, clinging to childish notions in a world that desperately needs adults, is it only mental patients that I am describing?

Psychiatry has this amazing opportunity. It can focus on any
part of the human line and learn there what will help the other
parts. It can study faults and flaws of human behavior in extreme and exaggerated form, so that warning and help may be
given to those in whom the same weaknesses are hidden and
apparently harmless. "Every man bears within himself the germs
of every human quality," and, therefore, the successful man with
one prejudice has much to learn from a mental patient with
one delusion. The fearful man may find courage in the fact that
the frightened mental patient may be cured. The man cursed
with an intolerant spirit may learn to love and forgive. Wherever
there is a successful attempt to understand the motives of individuals anywhere along the line, that understanding may
spread to encompass all mankind. And this is truly what psychiatry is for—to understand, to forgive, if possible to heal.

While the psychiatrist may not be the best person to describe
or define mental health, he holds certain advantages. Someone
once said of an artist, "He has lucid moments when he is only

stupid." In other words, the abnormal and disordered mind may reveal more than can be read in the poker face of the normal man whose conduct and emotions are under control. It is difficult to study the normal man because he is, quite properly, a closed book. He shuts himself up; he is polite; he minds his own business and makes it his private business. The man who is abnormal, for the moment or for a long time, is wide open; he is split and shows the lines of cleavage. This may be embarrassing exposure, but it can give us some useful understanding of the normal person, even if it is not complete.

The experience of a psychiatrist may be helpful to clergymen, educators, and physicians, who all need a sympathetic understanding of their difficult, unreasonable, and unusual parishioners, pupils, and patients. What mental patients and people under stress say may unlock the silences which surround many healthier minds. It is possible, indeed, that some of the chapters which follow may persuade husbands and wives, parents and children, to take a different view of those of the family who, for some strange reason, do not always and altogether agree with them.

This is not a self-help book, not an exhortation, but an invitation to the intelligent reader to take a look just beneath the surface at himself and the people about him—under the masks, the camouflage, the screens that are so universal and so efficient in deceiving the unalerted eye. What I hope for is vision such as one gets in a low-power microscope, which misses what a high-power microscope reveals, but has a value all its own. The high-power vision must be left to psychiatrists, therapists, and analysts, who can give years to one person if necessary.

In a city map we can see, as in a high-power magnification, all the streets and bridges and parks. A map of one small area on a large scale may show individual buildings. But in a map of the United States, as in low-power vision, one sees a large or small dot which represents the whole city, gives no information about its streets or houses, but does place it in relation to the rest of the country.

I have been told and, in general, I agree that books should state a theory and then prove it. The reason I can't fit this book into this pattern is that I have little confidence in my theories and much confidence in my facts. Scientists say that facts by themselves are of little account, that the meaning of facts and their place in a theory are all that matters. I am not sure of this, but I am sure that facts in a series are important. And that is what my "line" or your "line" really is. I hope I have presented my facts in such a way that readers can put their own facts beside them and then arrive at their own conclusions and theories.

This hope is supported by a statement of the philosopher George Santayana, then aged eighty-eight. "I never wanted to lead anyone. I am not a moralist who likes to admonish. I have simply tried to be a communicative student of the effects of things on people." *

A report to the American Public Health Association has said that "one-third of our adult population consists of unhappy, ineffective and upset persons who pose an extremely high burden of expense for the rest of society." One-third means many millions—perhaps twenty or more million men and women in this country alone. The "expense" must be measured in many things besides money: in tired nerves and tattered tempers, in unhappy homes and miserable marriages, in idleness and inefficiency. Surely no nation can be considered sound and strong if one-third of its people are sick in heart and mind!

* Laurence Dame, "Last Interview," *Harvard University Bulletin*, Nov. 10, 1956.

Chapter II

A LINE OF SOMEWHAT
NORMAL PEOPLE

CHAPTER I has led logically, I hope, to the foundation of this book—a line of men and women arranged according to the degree of mental health which I think is in them.

Each individual sketch has an importance by itself and another meaning as part of a series. I know that the assignment of positions is arbitrary, but it is of use as a target. And no matter how much the units are rearranged, the line will help to bring out some basic conditions of human nature and, especially, to throw light on what is meant by the word normal. If there are degrees of normality, what are they?

Again arbitrarily, I have put percentages before the sketches of these individuals as a constant reminder that there is some order in the line.

As I remember the people I have known personally or through their friends and relatives, I think of a family album—everybody's family on its white pages—a "family of man." I hope that every reader will feel close to the happinesses, the predicaments, and the failures which will be portrayed.

Some may believe that they recognize themselves in these pages, or a relative, friend, or neighbor. They will be wrong, although I decline to use the weasel phrase employed by authors and publishers of novels and television drama that any resemblance between my sketches and other persons, living or dead, is "purely coincidental." While all sketches are sufficiently disguised, there is a more important protection against recognition, and that is a fundamental idea in this book. For every example used, there are dozens more in the files. Resemblances are not coincidental but inevitable. An amazing discovery in the practice of psychiatry is that a sophisticated society lady from New York City will have the same symptoms, expressed in similar words, as a farmer's wife from an isolated western ranch.

100% (?)

Many believe that Albert Schweitzer, musician, philosopher, theologian, physician to Africa, is the greatest living man. But John Gunther, writing of Schweitzer's wonderful work, hastens to call him "dictatorial, pedantic in a peculiarly Teutonic manner, irascible," and adds that "if he did not have defects he would be intolerable." William Hazlitt had this idea when he wrote, "It is well that there is no one without a fault, for he would not have a friend in the world." Another thinker, the Marquis de Fontanes, was bold enough and wise enough to warn Napoleon that "the desire for perfection is the worst disease that ever afflicted the human mind."

An educator once described a perfect child to a group of parents; they thanked him for the warning. Later I shall discuss the constructive and destructive sides of perfectionism. But here are statements of two men which arouse thinking on the subject. "I can't quit when a job is imperfect, even cutting the grass, and I have suffered for years with a burning pain in the forehead between my eyes which keeps me from working too hard." "My son is morally perfect, but he always has a pain in his stomach which keeps him from doing too much."

With these quotations backing me up, I can say that I have never known anyone who could be proved perfect, and I should distrust anyone who came bringing the proof in his hands. Most admirable people have some endearing young faults, and I am glad to turn to delightfully imperfect people.

90%

At the top of my list is a mother-in-law, and I know of her only through her son's wife. This young woman, exhausted and irritable after nursing her husband and children through long illnesses, was ordered by her doctors to take a rest away from home. She said, "Let me go to my mother-in-law. She loves me, and she lets me alone." What more does anyone need to know about a woman who must have encouraged independence in her son and who welcomed his wife into her own warm affection? To be sure, she was always "jittery" when she was away from her home, where she felt very safe. But her daughter-in-law rushes to her defense. "I know how she feels, but if I had asked her to come and help me she would have come at once."

Beside this woman stands a man successful in business, ambitious. He married late, and before his marriage—not after—he was a heavy drinker. He had two children and, because he thought he had too much aggressiveness in him, he left their discipline to his wife. His children think of him as strong and affectionate. After the birth of the second son he gave the first much attention, which is not too common an occurrence. He and his wife allowed no likes or dislikes for food in the children or in themselves. He had the same respect for the children as he had for himself and his wife. The children testify to a satisfying family life.

This man had aggressiveness in its old, or root, sense. Dr. Frederick Allen mentions a nice ancient saying: "Behold him aggress and come into his own." This man came into his own and can defend his own; he can also defend the rights of other people. But the usual, or destructive, meaning of aggressiveness does not apply to him, because he controls the desire to push other people around. As we go down the line we shall see more of destructive aggression that is less controlled and appears as domination, resentment, a wish to destroy and to kill. And we shall see that the more normal you are, the more you acknowledge and manage the aggression that is in you.

80%

Miss Case is a thoughtful, pleasant, conscientious woman of fifty with a sufficient income. She has artistic ability and enjoys her artist friends. She is responsive to the pleas of well-established community charities. But she is bothered by one thing—the need to save clippings. She is interested in so many civic, medical, and philosophical matters that her clippings pile up. She knows that she can never read them, but she keeps up her files and constantly adds to them. All in all, she leads a pleasant and a useful life, with one neurotic trait wasting some of her time and causing some distress of mind.

"You see many people much worse than I, as I have my feelings of lightness and joy. I love my house and my books. But I still find it hard to rest quietly instead of working on those infernal clippings." Surely a part of her mind is off on an unreasoning activity of its own.

Beside this nice woman stands Mr. Bowers, a kind son and husband, active in community and church affairs. His mother, now ninety, has always made excessive demands upon him and now lives with him. She is very deaf, and it is so difficult to tell her where he is going and when he is coming back that he often stays at home when he would sooner not. He cannot bear to hurt her feelings, and he sympathizes with her real troubles. When an automobile knocked him down, something unusual came out into the open. "I nearly struck mother. I was rude to my secretary. Although sometimes I hardly knew who I was, I raged all the time. I had projectile vomiting." (It did not project the resentment toward his mother which he had long refused to acknowledge.)

79%

I use this ridiculous percentage to confess and call attention
to my inability to place these "exurbanites" * and suburbanites.
In New York, Boston, and Philadelphia there are out-of-towners
who work hard and efficiently from 9 A.M. At 5 P.M. or there-
abouts comes a welcome time for relaxation with a few good
friends—all men—and a few good drinks. Then comes a tiresome
ride home; then cocktails.

At dinner and in the evening there may be one of two results.
The men are either sleepy and dull, or irritable and quarrel-
some. But the next morning at nine they are back in their offices
and ready for hard work. So business gets their best hours, and
their wives and children get the worst part of the day. There
is a homosexual slant in this, although the men would become
panicky if they had the slightest suspicion of it.

70%

Different kinds of neuroses are illustrated by brief sketches
of a dieter, a withdrawer, and a parlor revolutionist; they speak
for themselves.

"I am nauseated most of the time," says one of them. "It is
disgusting to think of, or talk about, digestion. . . . the *Reader's
Digest* is a revolting name for a magazine."

"I am bored by religion," says another; "I have dropped my
music; I am bored by my stomach symptoms, by books, by everything. I don't like my house, I don't like Philadelphia. I am bored
by my husband. But while my outside energy stands still, my
insides boil. A savage fights or runs away, but I do neither."

A third has a different kind of neurosis. "My father is so re-

* See A. C. Spectorsky, *Exurbanites*. J. B. Lippincott Co., Philadelphia, 1955.

spectable, so conservative, so reactionary! I am for the down-and-outer. I don't need my family any more than a mouse needs a cat. I am different, that's all. In 1927 I applied for membership in the Socialist party, and they turned me down. Things are upside down; why do I have to set them right? [Almost, we note, she is quoting Hamlet.] I'm tired of being the only honest person in Philadelphia. I want to throw a plate through a window. I want to lead a procession of revolutionists down Broad Street and throw a brick at the Union League. Oh, how I hate banks! Better to die in a revolution than to live among bankers! Put the Capitalists in prison."

As I write this I am watching a young woman who is walking toward our outpatient clinic over a long diagonal path which no one else is using. She takes two steps ahead and then one step backward, a typically neurotic way of getting anywhere—bizarre, foolish, uneconomical of effort. In this morning's paper I find a sentence in a British newspaper: "Mr. Dulles in his characteristic manner takes two steps forward and then one back." An American comment in another article says, "Mr. Eden takes two steps forward and one back." In the near future some diplomat will undoubtedly be accused of taking two steps forward and three back! Is diplomacy a neurosis? Apparently there is something in common between the woman bringing her personal emotional problems to a clinic and the wise men who bring great issues to the forum of world opinion.

A boy of fourteen was left, at the death of his parents, with a sufficient income but many fears about his physical and moral health. At twenty-two he married a woman who could stand between him and both sides of his fear—she was a trained nurse and also the daughter of his rector. At forty-two, never having worked at anything, he is in robust physical health, while his wife has an illness which will be fatal. As he tries to protect her, his own fears are diminished. For the first time in his life he is of some use to another person.

60%

Do misers and homosexuals belong here? I don't know.

I used to see a miser who wore a smashed-in derby hat and a tail coat in which the holes were made conspicuous by an inner lining of newspapers. This man left his millions to two of our finest and most valuable educational societies.

I know a homosexual who was distressed by his situation and was trying to help himself and others, but without much success. "Kinsey thinks homosexuality is normal, but I think it is a neurosis; I am interested in values, as he isn't. I think homosexuals like me have the same obligations to society that all men do. I hate my wife. I want to build a bridge to the heterosexuals. We are all part of the human predicament. I have constant anxiety and pains."

50%

At this point in the line I am more sure of my placements. There are two kinds of people at this level, and two clergymen show the contrast between them. In one, opposite currents were mixed; in the other, the opposite flows were separate.

The first had low standards. He kept his cruelty secret for practical reasons; he was clever in covering his tracks. He had enough faith in his religious ideals to keep him going in his church work. His good points were just sufficient to keep his vicious attributes from doing damage. He became a balanced neutral, so that there was nothing left over to give others. He had little struggle within himself because he was content to get by. He aroused little interest and no sympathy.

The second was a pathetic human being. In him there was a strong faith, a religious feeling which he made others share, a willingness and ability to help others, an appealing personality. But in him there was also a desire "to lie down in the gutter," "to be a bum," to follow and materialize the sexual visions which often haunted him. Here was no mixing of currents, but a heart-rending struggle for a man's soul. The last time I heard of him he was in the gutter; he may have risen from it by now. Everyone who knew him was drawn to him in his agony, though none could help him.

Many alcoholics are like this tragic man. One that I know was able in business, a hard worker with an outgoing personality. But he had a tendency to become intoxicated at the most inopportune moments, a weakness which became more pronounced as his position in business advanced. One night his friends drove him home, put him to bed, and took his car keys. When they left he got up, found duplicate keys, sent his car down a steep hill into a tree, and was found unconscious, with broken vertabrae and ribs. Yet he ran his business very well from his hospital bed.

45%

There are five men whose friendship I value greatly. They stand for over-all healthy-mindedness; they think and work constructively. They are leaders in good citizenship. They are a lawyer, a college president, a vice-president of a large manufacturing plant, a head of a vast charity, and a teacher.

They have all had depressions sufficiently serious to bring them to a psychiatrist for advice or treatment, and I present them as they are during their depressed times.

Here is what they have said. "I can't decide; I can't get going; I can only make doodles. Everything is black." "I haven't any courage; am I a weakling? I just go through the motions. I can't sleep." "I have been having definite periods of depression, often with real or imaginary physical ailments. There is in the back of my mind a kind of a sour taste, a dread of future duties. I feel I can't stand things, but I don't know what I mean. I wish I had a motor to get me out of bed in the morning. A cloud hangs over me." "I am not much good; I torment myself." "I looked at my work, and it wasn't interesting; I tried to read, and the book was flat; I sat down to eat, and there was no appetite. And I thought that these things couldn't all change the same way at the same time, so it must be me. I am selfish and all wrapped up in myself."

Now notice what their friends, their partners, their co-workers and families said about these men.

"A lawyer with a great sense of community responsibility." "The most wholesome influence in the community and in the college." "The spark plug of our whole business; he is worth any two of us who are his partners." "The only man whom all of our group will follow; he always does the right thing." "A teacher who thinks only of his pupils, never of himself."

These fine men whom I know, the salt of the earth, manage to carry their depressions for short times, though the times do not seem short to them. When they are out of the blues they work doubly hard, to all hours of the night, and have great activity and enthusiasm employed in useful ways. They have normal upswings.

The depressions sometimes seem to be nature's way of enforcing a rest, a lying fallow. Always, they give these men a quick sympathy with anyone who is suffering. These men have a lifelong and well-deserved success. We catch them in the line at their lowest ebb, and tomorrow they will move toward the top. Perhaps it is more accurate to say that these five men have an up-and-down temperament, while the next to be described have a definite up-and-down illness. As before, I take the down side first.

Here is a woman who, at the age of forty-five, had the "bottom drop out" of her life. Before that age she "had no fear in her make-up," was aggressive, full of energy, a businesswoman with a salary of $15,000 a year. After forty-five she became panicky and unable to make decisions, though she was still involved in responsibilities which required her to make them. She states her situation clearly.

"I feel something foggy in the front of my head. My thoughts are like a squirrel in a cage. I can keep in simple household ruts, but a new problem floors me. My mind goes so far and then stops. I concentrate just so long, and then the curtain comes down. I don't live—I just fool other people by going through the motions. My husband is wonderful and undemanding. But I am selfish, unloving, mean. I have a quirk which makes me want to give the wrong answers. I am my own worst enemy."

The shift from a depression can be seen in Mrs. A. In my regular hospital rounds I came upon her sitting almost motionless in a chair in a convalescent hall, with a frozen look of sadness on her face. She said, "I feel horrid, perfectly wretched. I feel that things aren't going on right around here. I see a gray curtain in front of me, or a cloud, a fog. There is a bad taste in my mouth." After two minutes she began to speak of some unimportant matters in a natural manner and with a normal expression, but this phase lasted barely a minute. Then her eyes began to sparkle, her manner became flirtatious, and she said, "You know, I have gypsy blood in me." I took her hand and began to lead her back to a room where her excitement would not be bothersome to other patients. She came along willingly, talking all the way. "I've made money on my voice—my husband paid me $25 to stop singing. If I raise hell, I get attention." She continued constant talking and loud singing, spitting, spilling food, always in violent motion, always distractible, for a month. Then she suddenly dropped back into the sad quietness in which I had first found her.

35%

Miss X. had been a healthy, bright, and sociable girl, very conscientious and high-strung. She graduated from college to take a position as principal of a private school for girls. After the sudden death of her mother, she also kept house for her father and two brothers. One brother was killed in an accident while she was nursing the other through a long illness.

At the death of her father, when she was forty, she suddenly changed. She became agitated and declared that she had no money, and no stomach. "I am guilty, guilty, guilty; I have ruined my body; I have syphilis; I am inbred. I have a baby here by myself or by my father; I am not Mrs. X., my father's wife. I am so little and am to be put down a drain in the bathtub; lots of people go up and down in that drain." And further, in a grandiose vein, "I have locked up the world."

After two years of these delusions she became busy at games and occupational therapy, repeatedly saying, "I can't walk, move, or talk; I'm not here." But after five years she began to read and said, "I wish I could be like I used to be." And after eight years she was well; she has lived normally for the past fifteen years.

25%–15%

Now come examples of those who have retreated, for want of a more comfortable place, into their own private worlds.

Angela had been a sunny, docile, and imaginative child. At the age of four she was immensely jealous of a new baby and prayed that it would die. It did, and she thought, "Perhaps I am a murderer." At four or five she was the child who made up all the games played by her group.

"I was always the leader, the queen of the fairies. I was careful not to touch a child with my wand for fear he would be turned to gold. I felt that my mother and most people were too practical. I didn't like to read novels because they were so true to life." At nine she published some poems and thought, "I am a genius." She became arrogant and domineering, and, because the family accepted her own estimate of herself, she was put under a governess so that she would not be contaminated by a school. When she was fourteen her father died, and she said, "All great people have something like this happen to them in their youth." She never tried to make any friends. She daydreamed instead.

At sixteen and seventeen she failed college board examinations, and her balloon came down. She cried; she wanted to enter a convent; she considered suicide.

Then daydreams turned into delusions, as water turns to ice. "I am pregnant by somebody through thought transference; everyone is looking at me." Admitted to a mental hospital, she said, "Just give me a room where I can dream away the rest of my life. Dreams are so much better than reality."

In contrast to this gentle behavior there is the utmost in

boy was "a gentleman, the favorite of the
one." He was mercilessly tormented physi-
sister. He was taught by tutors, who found
issive. At seventeen he went abroad with
ssy." Up to this time he had been on the
thing.

he took up every masculine aggressive
ing, hunting, riding, shooting, football,
rhea. His favorite author was Rudyard
to enlist in the Marines, Gene Tunney
nd heavyweight champion. He fought
began to hear God's voice—"or his fa-
er dead. At different hospitals for men-
veryone in sight, patients, nurses, and
t until I have fought every man in the

10%

A retired minister, eighty years old, had shown signs of advancing brain disease for ten years. In spite of an almost total loss of memory, and though troubled by a notion that he should go to a conference in another city, he was an example of gentleness and good will. Sometimes he did not know who he was. He couldn't recognize his children; he had no reason in him. Almost, but not quite, he had "lost his mind" completely.

0%

Finally there are some people, usually of advanced years, in whom brain damage has cut off the thinking part of the mind from the vegetative functions. They need nursing; they are bedridden; they are "sans everything."

Chapter III

THESE STRANGERS
ARE OURSELVES

WE HAVE BRIEFLY considered groups of people arranged in an order that began with the most and ended with the least normal. Secondly, individual cases were selected from those groups to give reality and vividness to certain positions in the line, and also to furnish a definite target to shoot at.

One criticism of this procedure may be made, and I am aware of it. While I feel sure about the positions of those at the top and bottom of the line, I am doubtful about those in the middle. But no matter how many rearrangements may be made, there will always be a line; in the imaginary alignment of all adults in the United States the gaps would be filled with hundreds, thousands, or millions of individuals, and transitions would be smooth from one person to the next on either side.

Even those far apart in our list have common problems. A strong man (90 per cent), in good health, was able to look directly at his great aggressiveness and then control it. A delicate man (80 per cent) was not able to see his own aggression, but buried it until it came out blindly and uselessly after he received a blow on the head. A young man (15 per cent), cruelly tormented in childhood and ruthlessly held powerless for seventeen years, his aggression deeply repressed, finally lost all control and killed. Like many revolts, his started in a proper direction but went too far. Is it too far from normal to break blindly out of an intolerable situation? To give aggression its head like a runaway horse?

23

In this connection I think of Mary Tree. She probably inherited a lively imagination from her mother, who was a poetess, and from her father, who had delirium tremens. She read many romances. She married early to escape her mother's impracticality and her father's drinking.

But her husband turned out to be dismal, rigid, and absorbed in his business. He spent evenings working over his inventories, never going to anything. The pair lived in a commonplace double house in Philadelphia, on the side away from the sun. They had no children. Resenting something his wife said, her husband refused to speak to her for six months and made her carry all his meals up to his second floor room, where he ate alone.

Mary suddenly ran away into a winter's night and was found by police half frozen in Fairmount Park. She was brought to a mental hospital, and she herself can tell what happened.

"I suddenly realized that I was not married. [Anyone who knew her husband could understand why she had that particular delusion.] I took my maiden name, Mary *Tree*. And then I remembered my real wedding long ago, which I never understood until now. We were swinging in an old apple *tree*; why didn't I recognize what that meant? Anyway, something was said about a courthouse, and we were married, and it was Sir Beerbohm *Tree*, and I've been Lady *Tree* and I haven't known it. . . . My true husband visits me at night; he is so romantic! This morning a child was born, but the nurses took it away."

The nurses in the hospital said, "Why on earth should she want to get well? Her new private world is so much better than her reality." A symbol of her new happiness was the nurses cheerfully carrying *her* meals to *her* second floor room.

But no matter how far up the line a person is stationed, that person can say, "This schizophrenic patient has the same wishes I have, is pulled by the same needs, rationalizes as I do. She is like me, *only more so*." Consider what it was that Mary Tree wanted and compare it with what other, more normal, women want. She wanted to get out of her unhappy first home and her unhappy marriage—and she did. She wanted a husband who had some romance in him; she wanted children; she wanted to be waited on once in a while. A woman with these same desires might be found at the top of our list.

A parallel case, with a happy difference, is that of the superintendent of a large psychiatric hospital who had wanted in his youth to enter Annapolis and the Navy, but was thwarted in his ambitions by a physical defect. His hospital became a ship, and he was the captain in an appropriate uniform. The physicians were officers in uniform; the nurses and attendants were noncommissioned officers; and the patients were both crew and passengers. There were Navy salutes and protocol. The hospital was well enough run, though the physicians were sometimes embarrassed to be taken for a band when three or more went out of the hospital together. But the superintendent and many of his patients had their own comfortable private worlds, like Mary Tree's.

In Chapter II Mrs. A. was given a place in the line as a representative of those who have changes of mood. So do we all. Have you watched the home crowd leaving the football field after an unexpected victory? Have you seen the same crowd after an unexpected defeat? Dr. Arthur Light, who used to be physician to a football team, tells me that after a Saturday defeat he learned immediately of all the bruises and sprains suffered by the players. But after a victory he had to wait until Monday or Tuesday.

An idea worth entertaining in this connection is that a business or a family would do well to have a depressed person as a buyer and an exhilarated one as a seller, or should arrange for one who would buy only in depressions and sell in up-moods as they came along.

Let me introduce here, as a special interest of mine, a marvelously compact group of individuals who have broken down in mid-life and combine the most fantastic delusions with an intact and witty intelligence. These patients have pre-illness characteristics which are often found in us all in everyday life and especially those who are going to retire some day or change their main occupation.

The technical term, involutional depression, fits this group well. I gave one example in the case of Miss X. Most of those who break in this manner have been punctilious, set, exact, living between rigid boundaries rather shut off from the main and less perfect world. They can be meticulous and routine in such employments as drug making and dispensing, in accounting, in protecting milk and water supplies for the public's benefit. They may get along well enough in a deep groove of family habit. But when change must come, when the groove is blocked by a death or by the marriage of children, by the loss of a job, or even by promotion to a new job, then many of these people cannot adapt to the change and break down in a set and familiar way.

A man of forty-nine, rigid, precise, and penurious, had never made a mistake in arithmetic at school and regularly had a grade of 100 per cent. He was at the top of his class at college. After he graduated, a remarkably suitable job was given him—the treasurership of a large university. But he could delegate nothing to others. For twenty years he went along without a mistake, but in his own way. Then the growing university needed an entirely new system of accounting and promoted him to a vice-presidency. He broke, came to a hospital, and began to give voice to amazing delusions.

The word "amazing" is justified by the way in which these delusions of different patients converge on death, nihilism, denial (especially of bodily organs), and on smallness or grandiosity. These typical quotations are from different patients.

"I seem to be quite dead."

"I had a lovely funeral."

"I died centuries ago, and I want to go to heaven in a Buick."

"I am nothing in the air."

"I have no face, no eyes, just holes."

"All the organs are out of my body."

"All my organs were taken out and burned in a solid gold kettle." (Note that an ordinary kettle would never do.)

"I am the Devil. Hosts of angels execute my commands."

"I am 6,000 years old. I knew Noah."

"Pharaoh, Nero, Caesar—I used to know all of them."

And from all such patients come reiterations of "can't" in countless variations. "I can't walk, talk, eat, love anyone; I can't stay, and I can't go."

These revealing phrases frequently come from patients who are keenly observant of everything that goes on around them and can step out of character at any moment for an aside. One of them said, as she noticed that I was writing down some of her remarks, "I am supposed to be crazy, but if you take down any more of the trash that I am saying, you are crazier than I am."

Vividly these patients say to all of us, "Prepare for change. You can't hold back the clock. You cannot build any exact little fortress of your own and hold it against the onslaughts of time, of new invention, of advance."

After adding these involutionists to the latter part of our line, it is well, for the same reason, to put somewhere in the middle the personalities of those who center their thoughts on their digestive functions. They are intensely occupied with diet fads, selection of eatables, bowel functioning. They try to take charge of a digestive process that would manage very well if left to itself.

This college girl of twenty-one is almost unbelievable, but she is, unfortunately, typical. Fully able intellectually to do college work, she missed her degree because she starved herself into illness. Claudia was an unplanned-for child; her mother wept and vomited all through the pregnancy. But when Claudia was born, her mother preferred her, while her father made much of a fat sister. When Claudia was three, the parents were divorced. Before then Claudia had fretted at breast feeding, had intestinal troubles, refused the bottle, and up to the age of five would take only semisolids and these only if her mother would hold her on her lap for hours. Always unsociable, she ate sparingly of a few foods, which had to be cooked by her mother or herself. At college she refused to eat in the dining hall and tried to live on what she bought and prepared for herself in her room. She left college and went back to her home, retirement, and her mother's cooking.

Another woman, now forty-eight, had feeding difficulties from birth. She cannot remember ever being free in childhood from some digestive disturbance which produced diarrhea and constipation by turns. At twenty-three, with her conscience almost as disturbed as her bowels, she decided to go to Japan as a missionary. At the last moment she was kept at home by typhoid fever, of all diseases the most gastrointestinal. On her recovery she entered the life of a pampered invalid. Every time she tries to do something for others or herself, she has nausea and vomiting.

It may be evident, therefore, that I approve of parents who are careful not to encourage food fads and fancies in their children.

Again, there is the case of a man of fifty who, at twenty, began to "watch" his digestion. He made the rounds of doctors and often prescribed for himself. He did good work at his office, but at mealtimes, in the evenings, or on vacation he held forth to his family and friends on the state of his stomach and bowels. At forty he began to ask the surgeons of his own city to operate. After careful study of his symptoms, they refused. At forty-nine he went to a distant city and persuaded a surgeon to remove his gallbladder, which turned out to be normal. He refused to leave the hospital, because he was convinced he had a cancer of the intestine. His abdomen swelled, he refused to eat, and he finally died of inanition. At autopsy no trouble of any kind was found except starvation, which he had imposed upon himself despite all the doctors said or did for him.

Another man, John, was bright, with an IQ of 123. He had a pouting, babyish mouth and was very gentle, soft, and considerate. He had "always" taken pennies from his mother's pocket-book to buy candy; in his early teens he had been insatiable in demands for cigarettes, gum, eatables. Some of his friends called him an "all-day sucker." He is now earning a good salary, but is in a precarious financial and social position. He is heavily in debt, not only for food and drink, but also for the pure pleasure he gets from spending money for what he wants, whether he needs it or not.

Our line may have a special value for those who have to do with courts of law, which means very many of us, as well as for doctors and psychiatrists who sometimes serve as "expert witnesses." The notion that people can be arranged on a line, with the most normal at the top, runs counter to the practical, legal idea of sanity. Webster's definition of sane is "sound and rational in mind," which might help if we had trustworthy definitions of "sound" and "mind" and did not know that there is no one who is fully "rational"—no one who has absolutely no prejudice, no one who has not put unreasoning emotion into some of his family and business decisions.

But lawyers must have clear-cut decisions as to sanity. It would be ridiculous to call a will or a deed to property 70 per cent valid. The lawyers and the courts must protect heirs and owners of properties. Legally, therefore, there must be an answer to the embarrassing question, "Is this person sane?"

My suggestion is to add the word "enough," which would reconcile legal need with the idea of degrees of normality. "Is he sane *enough* to sign the will, to complete this simple transaction, to solve this complicated problem?" This is probably taken for granted in court procedure and in the minds of judges, but a clearer statement would allow witnesses more ease and freedom to describe the *amount* of normality they find in a given person, leaving law officers to decide whether that normality is enough to make a person legally sane under the circumstances.

It is puzzling to a psychiatrist, after testifying in an unopposed guardianship case that an eighty-year-old woman could not remember her children or her belongings and did not know where she was or what year it was, to be asked by the judge, "Do you recommend that a guardian be appointed?" It may be a legal requirement for him to ask, but it seems unnecessary to the psychiatrist.

One woman involved in court proceedings was too good to be sane. Quiet and gentle, she certainly had some delusions which centered about her own unworthiness. What got her into trouble was her refusal to take $10,000 for a property because she thought and said that it was worth only $8,000. The judge, appealed to by the relatives and afraid of the consequences of letting such unselfishness loose on the real estate market, properly appointed a trust company as guardian of her property. The house was sold for $11,000, and sanity was restored to the sensitive real estate market.

These cases and comments have been additional to the simple line of the normal, more or less, laid down in Chapter II. They have value for everyday life because they are observations about patients who exaggerate common human traits. They show that, whenever you look closely at any man in the line, you find ideas of use to all of us who are above or below him.

However, there is still need to show more clearly that the middle of the line has more than its share of great gifts which enrich the world. I have known, personally as well as professionally, many talented people who belong there, but I cannot make use of their histories because they might be recognized. So I turn to another line, which consists of individuals, real or imagined, who have appeared in print—in book, magazine, or newspaper.

Chapter IV

CHARACTERS
FROM PRINTED PAGES

NOVELS, plays, biographies and autobiographies, magazine and newspaper articles, written not by psychiatrists and not with psychiatric purpose, furnish real and imagined characters for a line that parallels the line of individuals drawn from a psychiatrist's notebook. Most of these characters are more interesting, more gifted, more striking than the average run of people, or they would not appear in print. They are found—most of them —near the amazing center of the line.

Saints and others who take religion much to heart are apt not to be well-rounded people; nor are artists, creative thinkers, or inventors. One part of them is so advanced that other parts have not caught up. They often have great faults which are forgiven because of their gifts. They often have unusual and unmitigated virtues for which they are punished.

The selection offered here is from my own library shelves and from innumerable magazines, which help to "hold the mirror up to nature" if we read them with this in mind. Doubtless the reader could make his own list of characters from entirely different sources. If he has got this far in this book he is becoming more and more aware of the part that mental disturbance or disease plays in literature of all kinds, from documentary drama to the current tragedy recorded on the newspaper's front page. Even more dramatically, it appears in fiction and in honest and confessional autobiographies. And it is stuff of which the better television dramas are made.

At the top of my list—not for their literary qualities, but because they depict very normal people—stand the characters in
Anthony Trollope's novels of a century ago. Especially in *Dr.
Thorne*, a nice solution is worked out for the love problems of
two young people who meet all requirements for normality and
are surrounded by other people just as normal. In the days of
overbearing paternal domination, Dr. Thorne "argued that the
principal duty which a parent owed to a child was to make him
happy." Trollope's stories go along like gently flowing rivers;
in our anxious days they are perfect for reading just before we go
to sleep.

Also, over a century ago appeared the slightly less normal figures of Mr. Pickwick and his friends. As they ramble around
England in horse-drawn chaises or on horseback, without much
thought or plan for tomorrow, Dickens shows us the value of
"sane nonsense" in characters who have their foibles and weaknesses.

But let us keep our normal, gentle, unexciting characters in
England and in the past. To recommend a modern novel for
portraying such people would be the kiss of death. For more
complicated characters I turn to up-to-date personalities who are
somewhat one-sided, and then to groups of our contemporaries
as described in *Time*, *Life*, and the newspapers.

First is the autobiography of a very one-sided man. *Confessions of an Individualist* is a book by William Henry Chamberlain, who carried individualism to its normal limit. At the age
of seven he made a dismal failure of learning to dance because
he was thinking all the time of the Russo-Japanese War. He
never wanted to do what other children did; he was a lone wolf.
In school he loathed accuracy, mathematics, games, and science. He nearly cut off his fingers in woodworking, and he never
learned to drive a car. When he was ten he read Gibbon's *Decline and Fall of the Roman Empire*, and he still rereads it every
Christmas. At eleven he translated medieval German history.

He worshiped men who swam against the tide and hunted for them in all his reading and studies.

At college he was an immature but earnest freethinker in a conservative setting. He was against chapel, sports, and science courses, and was allowed to scrape through on one lone course in science. But he won highest honors in the classics. In World War I he was a pacifist and, later, a Communist sympathizer. But when he was sent to Moscow for ten years, to the home of Communism, he became a bitter anti-Communist. He is now a distinguished writer about history in the making. In his youth he was an inner-directed * person, except that he had his tentacles out to discover society's opinions in order to go against them.

Mr. Chamberlain tells us these things about himself, in his autobiography. In modern student-aptitude tests he would have been ranked close to the top in verbal and very close to the bottom in mathematical ability. But he has developed his strong points and learned to live with his weak ones.

The second man is the hero of one of my favorite books, and he is one-sided in a more serious and more subtle way. In *The Last Puritan* there is a young man who is pictured as having only one fault. "He would have been perfect if he had stopped revising himself." He had the kind of conscience which I shall consider in Chapter XII—"a moral nature burdened and overstrung. . . . Nothing existed for him save that which his moral tentacles were ready to seize. . . . You showed him the most beautiful things and he made notes." †

This is a curious and elusive fault. It brought unhappiness to a man who was brave, dutiful, honest, steady, sincere, intelligent, a great athlete. An allowance must be made for the fact that the author, George Santayana, was brought up as a Catholic

* See David Riesman, *The Lonely Crowd*. Yale University Press, New Haven, 1950.
† George Santayana, *The Last Puritan*. Charles Scribner's Sons, New York, 1936.

in Spain and transplanted into a Protestant family in Boston. Nevertheless, the character of Oliver sharply outlines a person who "disowns the living forces of nature" or who enjoys none of the "morally neutral" things in life. In contrast to the real Mr. Chamberlain, this character from a book has the effectiveness of his strong points ruined by the insidious penetration of a destructive element.

From the innumerable examples of the moderately normal to be found in current journalism, I choose one each from *Time* and *Life* in their issues of January 24, 1955.

Time tells us, "A few years ago a Dallas company set up a new subsidiary with five brand new vice presidents installed in identical offices. Everything was peaceful until one used his expense account to replace his single-pen set with a two-pen set. Within four days all five worked their way up to three-pen sets. Then they went on to bigger and flossier names on the doors and other changes, until the president called a halt and brought everyone back to one-pen sets." *

Life says, "Congressman W. wants to return to high, rigid price supports" for farm products. He also wants the United States to get rid of its stored surpluses. "For these incompatible aims he has a magic solvent: sell the surpluses abroad." But the Congressman also wants "sound international relations and reciprocal trade," although "dumping" surpluses in other countries brings protests that we are ruining them. "No responsible Congressman can be for fewer production controls and higher supports, more dumping—and friendly relationship with other countries." †

Newspapers report that bankers from a Western state went to Washington to protest against extravagance in government. They arrived in time to protest against a proposal to cut down on new post offices for their state, this protest being the exact opposite

* Courtesy TIME; copyright Time Inc. 1955.
† January 24, 1955.

of the one they came to make. This inconsistency is so common, found in all groups of citizens and reflected in almost all lawmakers, that it is hardly newsworthy.

So the human beings who are at the top of our business and political organizations are not so consistent and reasonable as they might well be expected to be. But I, for one, am glad to live in a country where such inconsistencies are possible. "Consistency is a somewhat overrated virtue," and luckily neither of our two great political parties can lay claim to it.

Keeping to the present time and to living writers, I have in mind two plays and two books which have had an influence on me—an influence which grows as I reread them.

Lady in the Dark is an account of a remarkably successful businesswoman who has some unknown component in her thinking which keeps her away from happiness. Her lack of ease, her flight from love, and her tormenting indecision are shown to be the result of an "exquisite forgotten agony" of a child four years old. That this play carried this message on stage and screen and was enormously successful as musical entertainment is a tribute to Moss Hart, its sensitive author.

In *The Little Foxes* there is described an abnormal family disintegrating under the pressure of avarice. There is also a touching and beautiful picture of a tomboy girl reaching maturity as she stands at the foot of the stairs and looks up at her possessive mother, who has helped her sick husband to die. Lillian Hellman puts a declaration of independence into these words.

Mama, I am not coming with you. . . . I mean what I say. With all my heart. . . . I am going away from you. Because I want to. . . .

[And if I say no?]

Say it, Mama, and see what happens. . . .

[I won't make you stay.]

You couldn't, Mama. . . .

[Well, you have spirit. . . . Would you—would you like to sleep in my room to-night?]

Are you afraid, Mama? *

A beautifully told story is *Absent in the Spring,* by Mary West-macott, a pen name for the remarkable Agatha Christie. It concerns a woman whose children have all married. She is returning to her home in England from a visit to a daughter in India. Because a bridge is out up the line, she has to wait for days in a desert terminus of the railway. There is no one to talk to. Two Arabs at the inn speak no English, and she is forced to think about herself. The food is adequate but monotonous. There is nothing to read, no radio or television, and all she can do each day is to go out and look at sand dunes.

She begins to find out things about herself, as others have done in desert spaces. Her protecting devices fall away one by one. She sees herself as selfish, unperceptive, indifferent to the needs of her husband and children. She sees why the children have been glad to leave home. She realizes that her pretenses, rationalizations, and excuses are gone, and gone with them are her self-satisfaction and comfort. She makes many good resolutions. But, when the train comes in with books and magazines and people to talk to, she soon forgets in active, busy life the truth which idleness has taught her. Such a story may make all of us wonder whether we need the sand dune treatment.

The great success of Anne Morrow Lindbergh's latest book, *Gift of the Sea,* tells us how deeply and widely felt is the need to "get away from it all," to find and steady ourselves in thoughtful solitude. How many of us, like Anne Lindbergh, would bring back from the sands of the sea or desert (dunes again) the good resolutions and purposes and the insight we need to live happily and usefully in the real world? Or would we, like the woman in *Absent in the Spring,* soon forget after the train came in?

* Lillian Hellman, *The Little Foxes.* Random House, New York, 1939.

Now let us go back a few generations to four men in whom ran two opposing currents.

Thomas Carlyle was a vociferous, tremendous talker, demanding silence, which, according to him, was "deep as eternity." Intolerant, bitter, moody, self-centered, he described his fellow Englishmen as "twenty-seven millions, mostly fools." And yet he was a thinker, a prophet, a reformer, generous, transparently honest. A dyspeptic genius, construction and destruction struggled in him for mastery.

In Thomas De Quincey the downward urge is symbolized by his opium addiction. This man, who spent his youth in imaginary worlds of his own creation, always had to fight an urge for seclusion and obscurity, a flight from misery of any kind, to become a writer's writer, a force in today's literary world.

In English literature William Cowper, who would alternate between self-accusation for committing the unpardonable sin and spiritual ecstasy, and Charles Lamb were both productive men who were subject to mood swings.

It is not necessary to turn back for illustrations of the tragic countercurrents in great writers. Recent magazines and papers were full of comment on the death, at thirty-nine, of Dylan Thomas, the Welsh poet. One of his remembered sayings is, "I hold a beast, an angel and a madman in me, and my enquiry is to their working and my problem is their subjugation and victory, down-throw and upheaval." By the time he drank himself to death he had fully and tragically illustrated the three personalities which had struggled for dominance within him.

In the book review section of the New York *Times* of June 17, 1955, there are numerous references to the normality or abnormality of authors and the characters created in their writings.

Of editor-author Henry Mencken, it is said that he had "weird ideas about politics, religion, economics and races." Of author Ring Lardner, his "profound melancholy," the "silent vigils lasting for days and the benders lasting for months" are mentioned in describing a man of warm heart and amazing ability.

The painter Toulouse-Lautrec is defended as "one of the most courageous beings who have done honor to a worn-out civilization"—because he lived in a brothel! The "hero" of *The Ninth Wave* is declared to be strong, unscrupulous, a fearless fanatic, destruction personified.

Two deliberately psychiatric books are reviewed in the same section of the *Times*. The first deals with psychoanalytic studies of great men, an analysis of the nature of the creative process. The second is a book on Alfred Adler and his theory of inferiority and the struggle for power.

In the whole literary section the characters, real or fictional, described by reviewers belong in the middle of the line of normality—or below. And they are considered to be of interest to the general reader. It is equally astonishing that audiences in New York theaters are expected to be familiar with much of Freud's thinking.

A classic case of neurasthenia is Elizabeth Barrett, as portrayed in *The Barretts of Wimpole Street.** In the play made from the book her doctor says, "It's this increasing low vitality of yours that worries me. No life in you—none." And Elizabeth replies, "I wish Papa were a happier man." Says the doctor, "It's no business of mine, but when a man has good health, plenty of money, and a jolly family of boys and girls I can't see why he should make life a burden to himself and others." Elizabeth says, "Papa or one of my brothers carries me from my bed to the sofa in the morning and back to bed at night."

In the beginning of the book and throughout most of the play Elizabeth is portrayed as a rather irritating character, as she probably was during many years of her real life. But the reason for it is clear. Her more or less imaginary illness was a sacrifice to an erotic and possessive father, who was determined that none of his daughters should ever marry and much preferred Elizabeth as a hopeless invalid in bed. The love and energy of the young

---

* Rudolph Besier, *The Barretts of Wimpole Street*. Little, Brown & Company, Boston, 1930.

Robert Browning, six years her junior, gave her strength to live the normal life of a wife and mother. Once delivered from the dominance of her father, says one authority, her married life was "supremely happy."

The son of Oscar Wilde raises a strange question in his autobiography. Is the misbehavior of a brilliant, homosexual man more, or less, abnormal than the brutal and illogical punishment visited by the community upon his innocent wife and children?

Swings of mood are given their poetic due by Milton in "Il Penseroso" and "L'Allegro." The moods seemed to him like night and day, winter and summer. He could write, it is said, only in the summertime. The following lines are from "L'Allegro."

> Hence, loathed Melancholy,
>   Of Cerberus and blackest Midnight born
> In Stygian cave forlorn
>   'Mongst horrid shapes, and shrieks, and sights unholy!
> Find out some uncouth cell,
>   Where brooding Darkness spreads his jealous wings, . . .

This was one side of Milton's shield, the dark and depressed side. The other was gay with color, bright with sunshine.

> Sport that wrinkled Care derides,
> And Laughter holding both his sides.
>
>   .   .   .   .
>
> Quips and Cranks and wanton Wiles,
> Nods and Becks and wreathèd Smiles. . . .
>
>   .   .   .   .
>
> These delights if thou canst give,
> Mirth, with thee I mean to live.

The poet, with his inner knowledge, touches moods familiar to other creative men who have done their work in upswings and then apparently lain fallow in sluggish intervals.

For an inspiring example, a rare one, I turn to Joshua Logan, a commanding figure in our present literary world, who, curiously enough, was a patient in the hospital where I was medical director. That Mr. Logan is great enough to believe that a full and honest account of his mood swings may be helpful to others, I gather from an article in *Life* which evidently had his approval.

First let me take some words and sentences from an article entitled "No Let-Up for Logan," by Joseph H. Steele, published in the New York Sunday *Times*.*

From the moment he is on the set at 9 A.M. until the day's last scene is shot, . . . Logan is actor, writer, director, producer, photographer, sound engineer, prop man and every other technician on the set. He never sits still. He arrives on the scene looking immaculate. . . . By the time he has shot the first scene his clothes look as though they had never met an ironing board, his tie is askew, his shirt in chaos. . . . His concentration is so intense that his roving brown eyes look at familiar faces without seeing them. He listens without hearing, lost in intellect. . . .

On occasion when someone is tardy or noisy, or when there is palpable carelessness or unwarranted distractions . . . he will heap magnificent vituperations on the offender. . . . If a scene calls for dancing with no sound track handy, he will unhesitatingly burst into a song of the required rhythm, snap his fingers and wave his arms; and Will Holden, Rosalind Russell and Kim Novak dance to the Logan tune. . . . This tendency and faculty to play all the parts is, perhaps, the outstanding idiosyncrasy of this man of many facets. He reads the lines accompanied by appropriate intonations and facial expressions of every player, be he aged or juvenile, male or female. . . .

In his article Mr. Steele cites one bystander's observation: "If there is an Academy 'Oscar' for the best acting by a director, Joshua Logan would wrap it up!"

And in the *Life* † article: "On Broadway, Logan stands right now at the pinnacle of his profession."

* August 7, 1955.
† Lincoln Barnett, "Josh Logan," *Life*, May 9, 1948.

This is the Joshua Logan who has given joy to millions; for whose help in time of trouble Helen Hayes has been thankful. Once his up-mood was too much for him, as if his motor were racing. Again from *Life*: "Subtly, without realizing it himself, he swung from a depression into an opposite phase—an elation, a condition of great vigor and self-assurance." He did wonders with a stage production but "night after night he never slept at all." From here on he did not concentrate, but wandered about New York, gave a huge party to which only two invited guests showed up, became frightened, dizzy, and exhausted and "went on to Philadelphia to look for Dr. [Merrill] Moore," a friend and psychiatrist, who told him to go voluntarily to a hospital. Some hours later, after more wanderings, "he hailed a cab and collapsed in the back seat saying, 'Take me to the Pennsylvania Hospital.' "

Once in the hospital, "a wave of tranquillity enveloped him and he fell asleep." Logan remained in the hospital for three months, during which he rested as he "played baseball and golf, swam, studied Spanish and sculpture; wrote poems, stories and plays; composed music, painted and built a model theater and set type." But he slept well at night and was away from the fascinating demands of the real theater. Finally he lost his elation, and the doctors told him to go home.

I turn to a brilliant man who had good upswings and black moods one after the other. This was Ed Howe, "the greatest reporter in America," described by Gene Howe, his brilliant, moody son, in "My Father Was the Most Unhappy Man I Ever Knew." * Gene discloses why his father nursed an unreasoning, unrelenting hatred of religion that lasted to his death, and incidentally reveals the identity of a prejudice and a neurosis. Ed Howe's father was a circuit rider, "stern, unforgiving, and exacting," who brought up his children by the rod in puritanical rigidity. He would ride horseback from one church to the next

* *The Saturday Evening Post*, October 25, 1941, with permission of the Howe estate.

with his son Ed up behind him; he would preach five or six hours
and whip the boy if he nodded or fell asleep. Ed could not help
noticing his father's way with women members of his flocks;
finally, this "religious" patriarch ran away with one of these
women, abandoning his wife and several children.

Ed Howe hated religion all his life, and why? He had never
known what it was; he knew only his father.

But, aside from this prejudice-neurosis, Ed Howe had mood
swings. For six weeks at a time he would not speak, "his face
dark and forbidding, his wretchedness hardly believable." Then
his spirits would revive, and he would enter a period of exaltation,
happy and cheerful and walking on air with his head in the
clouds. "His joy of living would embrace everybody close to him.
Happy days were back, life was grand."

It is easy to understand young Howe's error in regarding whatever happened just before his father's depressions as their cause.
"Cancellations of advertising contracts, rebuffs, brought about
mental depressions." Almost everyone makes the same mistake
by failing to realize that an unknown, but inner, cause determines
both the downs and the ups of an illness or of a temperament.
Happy things can precede depressions; I recall one patient who
began a depression after unexpectedly receiving $100,000 from
an unknown uncle.

Chapter V

OLD TALES
WITH NEW MEANING

IN THE BOOK OF JOB we find an excellent description of involutional melancholia. Compare Job's words with those of present-day mental patients quoted in Chapter II.

. . . Job opened his mouth and cursed the day of his birth. . . . Why did I not die at birth, . . . my groanings are poured out like water. . . . I have no rest, but trouble comes. Oh, that my vexation were weighed, . . . For then it would be heavier than the sand of the sea; . . . I am allotted months of emptiness, and nights of misery are apportioned to me. . . . My flesh is clothed with worms and dirt; . . . my life is a breath; . . . I loathe my life; I would not live forever. . . . If I say to the pit, "You are my father," and to the worm, "My mother," or "My sister," where then is my hope? . . . My bones cleave to my skin and to my flesh, and I have escaped by the skin of my teeth.*

And Job, just as mental patients do, keeps referring to his body organs. His kidneys are "slashed open," his gall is poured out on the ground; he is shriveled up; his skin is hardened, turns black and falls from him, and his bones burn with heat.

It is remarkable that the present-day patient who is like Job talks repetitiously in terms of gloom, nothingness, emptiness, air, decay of body, with some grandiose thinking as an incongruous accompaniment.

* The Book of Job, Chapters 3, 6, 7, 17, 19. The Holy Bible, Revised Standard Version, Thomas Nelson & Sons, New York, 1953.

Schizophrenic thinking in literature is shown best in Grimm's fairy tales and in the Greek myths. Such thinking is daydreaming, plus a belief in the daydreams. It rejects reality and builds its own world. It follows patterns found frequently in fairy tales and myths, which often include intervention by witches, sorcerers, good fairies, and gods. It is checked by no practical considerations and by no conscience.

Here is, in brief summary, a tale of the brothers Grimm intended to be read to the gentle ears of children. A witch had two daughters, or rather, a daughter of her own, ugly and wicked, and a stepdaughter, who was lovely and good. The latter had a Sweetheart Roland to whom she could run in the night, a rather nice arrangement for a good girl to have. The good girl had a beautiful apron, and the bad girl wanted it. So the witch decided to cut off her stepchild's head. She told her own daughter of the plan for the night, but she was overheard by the proposed victim.

The bad girl went peacefully to sleep as soon as she was certain that some time in the night her sister, in the same bed, would have her head chopped off. In fact, she slept so heavily that the good sister was able to shove her about and change places with her, thus becoming an accessory to the murder. The witch-mother, as planned, came and chopped off the head of the girl on the outside of the bed and then went to her own bed and slept soundly.

It is curious what capacity for sleep the two wicked women had, while the good girl could not sleep at all, but finally got up and ran to her Sweetheart Roland, who was wise enough to send her back for the witch's wand. When she was stealing the wand, it seemed a good idea for her to carry her sister's head, still dripping blood, about the house. Then she rejoined her lover, and the two ran away. Next morning the witch was informed by voices from the drops of blood of what had happened and took after the runaways.

On the first night of the pursuit the girl changed her lover into a lake and herself into a duck swimming on it. On the second night, she changed herself into a white rose in a brier patch. When the witch reached for the flower she was forced to dance to the magic fiddle played by Sweetheart Roland until she tore herself to death on the brier thorns, thus becoming the second person whom the good girl helped to murder.

How can children take this kind of fairy tale in stride? I can think of partial reasons. It is a natural childish notion to abolish the person who frustrates. "Off with his head!" is a joke in *Alice in Wonderland,* and children enjoy it. Further, few children know death. In another well-known tale, Snow White is brought back to life or to wakefulness—sleep and death are the same thing. In children and in schizophrenics there is a fusion of contradictory notions of murder and morals, of "bloody earthiness" and a confused identification of human beings and minerals. Sweetheart Roland, we remember, was changed into a lake, and if a man can be changed into water why bother whether any person for the moment is alive or dead? Childish and schizophrenic thinking can float along without checks or boundaries and without reference to reason and reality.

How about the thinking of any author who has universal sympathy and all-encompassing imagination? He must disregard ordinary boundaries; he may become a man or a woman, live in the past or present or future, live as an old man or as an adolescent. He is in love with men and with women, with mother or sister. He re-creates the psychology of the myth; life is traced back to death, and the two are seen as interchangeable.

Fairy tale, myth, child, artist, and mental patient all think together, and perhaps in some unguarded moments we all join them.

The charming tales of Hans Christian Andersen have little in common with the gloomy, gory yarns of the Grimm brothers. They have their villains, dragons, witches, and cruel stepmothers, but the child who reads or hears them is never in doubt as to which are the "goodies" and which the "baddies."

I have no sympathy with those who have tried to modify Mother Goose so that little children will not get the idea of cutting off the tails of blind mice with carving knives, or stealing pigs and running away like Tom the piper's son. The jingles of Mother Goose are probably harmless, more so than some singing commercials on radio and television.

The myths of ancient Greece illustrate types of schizophrenic thinking in a more noble way, partly because they have come down to us through the writings of the great Greek poets and dramatists. They do not, I think, do justice to the Golden Age of Greece, when lived many of the greatest men and minds that the world has known. A fair question was asked many years ago in the title of the book *Is Mankind Advancing?* Its author noted that no other period in the history of mankind had produced so many philosophers, artists, architects, playwrights, statesmen, and thinkers as the three centuries of the Golden Age.

We might doubt this statement if we knew nothing of ancient Greece but the tragedies of Sophocles and Aeschylus. The reason for this may be that lighter forms of literature are the least enduring. There are Greek comedies, of course, but they are not very amusing now. Comedy is evanescent, ephemeral, and "dated." Much wit and humor die overnight, and only as museum pieces do we relish many of the comedies of the eighteenth and nineteenth centuries. Yet we must assume that the ancient Greeks enjoyed lighthearted laughter, as they loved beauty and created so much of it for their own satisfaction and for the imitation of centuries to come. But they left little of their daily fun on record.

On the other hand, the themes of tragedy—sorrow, suffering, fate, and conflict—are timeless and unchanging. Some can be readily traced from Broadway back to the amphitheater in Athens. Men suffer today as they suffered then, and the causes and occasions of their suffering are alike. "The world," said Sir Robert Walpole, "is a Comedy to those who think, a Tragedy to those who feel." So the tragic themes of the Greek stage are with us today, and some are part of our language. They are almost household words among analysts and psychiatrists, and even with the American people. "Oedipus complex," though usually used inaccurately, is a commonplace phrase in adolescent and collegiate conversation. The twisted, tragic tale of Oedipus and his family troubles has furnished plots for countless books and plays, and is now found in less forthright fashion in the plots of many television dramas.

The complications of the Oedipus myth may be outlined in respect to the person of Creon, rather than the better-known hero or victim of the tragedy.

Creon had a sister, Jocasta, who was married to Laius, King of Thebes. Oedipus was the son of Jocasta and Laius. Because Laius had been warned by an oracle that this son might endanger his throne and his life, he gave the baby to a herdsman to destroy in any way he pleased, with no questions asked. But the softhearted herdsman left Oedipus hanging by his foot from the branch of a tree, where another herdsman found him. We have here, as we shall see, a situation which many mental patients and many imaginative children commonly use.

Oedipus was taken to court and adopted by the King and Queen of Corinth, whom he believed to be his parents. But, trying to fight against his fate, he left them when he was told by an oracle that he would kill his father and marry his mother. On his wanderings he met Laius, his real father, and slew him in a dispute over the right of way. Creon had meanwhile become Regent of Thebes.

Later, as he approached Thebes, Oedipus met a Sphinx, part winged lion and part woman, which lay on a towering rock and asked a riddle which is still used to puzzle and amuse children. "What animal in the morning goes on four feet, at noon on two, and in the evening on three?" All travelers before Oedipus had been killed because they could not answer that man crawls on all fours in babyhood, walks upright in adult life, and uses a cane or staff to support his old age. The correct answer by

Oedipus so upset the Sphinx that she killed herself. In gratitude, Thebes gave Oedipus the throne in the place of Creon, and along with the throne went Queen Jocasta.

Is this really an ancient and remote parable about the small boy who wishes that he might marry his mother and get rid of his father—a recurrent discovery of the modern psychoanalyst?

To pursue a little farther the tragic consequences of the intermixture of humans, oracles, and gods, Jocasta committed suicide and Oedipus blinded himself when their true relationship became known. These characters, as I have said, were Creon's sister and his nephew–brother-in-law. Later, because of his blind anger, Creon's niece, son, and wife became suicides, while another son met a heroic death and a daughter was poisoned by the sorceress Medea. Creon himself was killed in battle. Murder, suicide, and morals are all entangled in this myth, even more than in the Grimm fairy tale.

A part of the same theme turns up twenty centuries later. In Shakespeare's *The Winter's Tale* another king sends a baby out to die, this time his daughter. Again the child is abandoned by a softhearted messenger, but this time on a desert shore, and the messenger makes the famous "exit, pursued by a bear"—the bear which later kills him. And again the child is raised by a shepherd and his wife. But she is "too noble for this place" and is found by a prince and restored to royal estate.

A patient in a hospital, just graduated from college, said to me, "I have discovered that I am not the son of my so-called parents in Chicago, but of royal birth and placed by my father the King with those humble people. I shall go to Europe and demand my proper station. I am [the same words] too noble for this place."

A woman patient told me, at a time when Austria-Hungary was still an empire, "I am a man, of course, and heir to the throne. My father, the Emperor, had to send me to this country as a baby because of plots against my life, and so I was brought up disguised as a girl. It is time for me to take my proper position in the world and to marry the queen of a neighboring state. Last night a golden airplane took me to see her. On returning, the plane flew right through the walls without making a sound, and I found myself in bed."

Parallels to the marriage-with-mother phase of the Oedipus story are numerous. One man, who had been sheltered by his widowed mother for forty years, married a young woman who strikingly resembled that mother. From her he expected protection and to be waited on; in the end, he went back to live with his mother. And I have encountered two schizophrenic men who kept mumbling, "I want to sleep with mama-mama-mama."

My friend Gregory Zilboorg reminds us of Proust's "Discovery of the Oedipus Complex." At the age of fourteen Proust was asked what was the greatest misery man could know; he answered, "Separation from Mamma." When Proust's father died, "his incestuous drives were pushed close to the surface." When a man he knew plunged a dagger into his mother's heart and, in trying to kill himself, shot out one eye, Proust saw "the eye of the unfortunate Oedipus."

Did Proust see or imagine this connection because he was as close to schizophrenia as one can get, with his mind filled with "murder, death, torture, submission to God and to the past," his body indolent and helpless—a "mannequin"?

All through the ages, poets with deep insight and writers who saw below the surface of things and people have described the tremendous forces which sway all human beings; and they have described them in words which no psychiatrist can command. Many more and many different examples of the "more or less normal" in literature might be given, and the reader may amend or improve my selection to suit himself. In half the books and magazines that we read and in every newspaper are passages which let us look, if we have attentive eyes, a little below the surface of human nature to the troubles and tragedies of the human mind.

It may be that preoccupation with psychiatric matters is a pass-

ing phase in current literature, reflecting the public's great interest
in a subject which has only recently become a universal theme
of thought and conversation. Even so, it can be useful and helpful if the reader bears in mind that, in stage, screen, or printed
stories, there is necessarily an element of overemphasis and even
exaggeration. Actors wear heavy make-up which would be ab-
surd and fantastic if worn on the street; otherwise their char-
acterizations would not carry through the glare of the footlights.
Authors often overwrite for the sake of drama and excitement in
their stories. In the same way literature gives us more striking
and startling "case histories" than are commonly found in
mental hospitals, or among normal people who are not in hospitals but share some of the mental patient's problems and difficulties. Actually, as has been said many times, most people are
more or less normal, not altogether good or bad, right or wrong,
admirable or contemptible, sane or insane. What has been said
in this book, therefore, may serve as a balance to some of the
gloom and pessimism found in current literature.

Far from being a review of plays, books, and other writings
that deal with matters in the psychiatric field, Chapters IV and
V have dealt only with items that I have accidentally come upon
while reading for pleasure or general information. Accidentally?
Yes, but with an experience with real people that made me
sensitive to the ways in which human nature explains itself. It
is not an accident to find what you are looking for most of the
time, even though it turns up when and where it is not expected.
Certainly, another reader of books and periodicals could duplicate my examples or improve upon them without reference to any
of the sources on which I have drawn.

Chapter VI

THE UNSOLVED PUZZLE
OF GREATNESS

IN THE LINE of the normal, more or less, the placements of patients and people I have known were based on firsthand information, since they have spoken for themselves or their close friends and relatives have spoken for them. Concerning characters in books and other printed matter, I relied on authors whose testimony may be considered secondhand.

Now I turn to thirdhand information in an attempt to place some great men where they belong on our scale. Their stories are mostly found in histories, encyclopedias, and other reference works.

But the undertaking is almost hopeless from the start. The great man is likely to be complex and many-faceted, and his greatness is partly his own, partly the product of unusual opportunity or environment. We see him in action on the wide stage of history, not in the doctor's office or the small world of the mental hospital. Sometimes we see him afar off, separated from us by centuries of changing ways and customs and surrounded by circumstances alien to our own. Do not expect, therefore, that I can suggest exact, or even approximate, places in the line for all those whom the world calls "great."

We do not know exactly what we mean when we say that a man is "great," though Carlyle, Emerson, and others have tried to tell us. Greatness is as hard to define as normality. Is it goodness and helpfulness, or notoriety, or eminence? Is it genius? Substituting the word "genius" for "greatness" does not help us

much, for there are amazingly many and varied definitions of
genius. It has been called madness, character, precocity, concentration, originality, uncommonness, patience, uniqueness. It
is said to be "doing what is impossible for talent." It is "an infinite capacity for taking pains."

Certainly greatness has something to do with inherited and
acquired abilities, something to do with environment and education, something to do with mental health and illness. But nobody has succeeded in writing a formula for it that will work,
though many educational fads are formulas for making something from nothing, or silk purses from very unpromising material.

Heredity is even more difficult to handle in synthesizing greatness, as is hinted in the legend of the beautiful and artistic woman
who suggested a eugenic alliance with a brilliant but unbeauti-
ful man. "With your brains and my face and figure," she said,
"our child would be perfect." The gentleman appreciated the
compliment, but turned down the offer. "It is possible," he
pointed out, "that the baby might be born with your brains and
my beauty."

In the majority of cases, heredity offers no clue to the source
or origin of greatness. The sons of Socrates, for example, never
amounted to much—which may have been their mother's fault
—and neither Shakespeare's ancestors nor his descendants left
any mark on literature.

We have discussed many educational and environmental conditions which are hurtful to mental and emotional growth. If
they were all avoided or eliminated, might we expect that there
would be more great men and women than there are? It would
be pleasant to think so, but the evidence seems to be against us.

Let us contemplate first some non-notorious, non-eminent,
undistinguished people whose names are very unlikely to appear in any list of great men, or even in *Who's Who in America.*
They are introduced to us in *Children of the Cumberland* by
Claudia Lewis.

Miss Lewis is a teacher who first taught in a nursery school in New York, where her pupils were "little hellions." School was a daily riot of tantrums, screams, fights, tears, wet pants, and resistance to every "must." But then she went away from the city and met the school children of the Tennessee hills. She was amazed to find them docile and well behaved. There was no rebellion, no maladjustment among them. Soon she came to realize that the typical mountain child had enjoyed a "period of long natural babyhood," close to father and mother, with "the privilege of suckling at the breast at any time, even long after he ate solid foods." He had lived in a house with no fragile things in it, no carpets or rugs. Toilet training was indifferent; there was no hurry about it, no insistence on washing or keeping clean. A father might be found singing to a group of his children in the middle of an afternoon. With an emotionally secure childhood, boys grew up in a society unusual in its non-competitiveness.

But this happy beginning "robbed them of that streak of neurosis almost indispensable for getting ahead in the world"; in other words, for getting into an encyclopedia or a list of great men. "It is a blessing if you call them content, or a curse if you call them shiftless," but whatever you call them is of supreme indifference to them. They do not know or care that you exist. There is no neurosis here—and no greatness.

It is not to be wondered at that Professor Cattell, in his *Study of Eminent Men*, chose as the only objective method of selecting or defining great or eminent men the measurement of the space they occupied in encyclopedias. By laboriously counting the number of lines devoted to people in six encyclopedias of the world, he was able to list a thousand persons in a definite order. If challenged as to the position of any individual, he could say, "show me a better way of determining it." This man had so many lines more than the next, and so he was "greater." This list has "objective impartiality and value"; but it attempts the impossible. Yet it is something to begin with in selecting a few great men for analysis and discussion.

A thousand names, of course, are too many. So from Professor Cattell's long list I took the top hundred, regretting that this ruled out or squeezed out some of my favorite people. Further help in shortening the list was given by my friend Herman Mehring, who brought me the book *Masters of Achievement* * which he had used in college. Employing another method of selection, the editor listed one hundred persons as the greatest of the great. They were chosen on the basis of "the opinions of past writers," "the best contemporary authorities," and "personal advisers of the first order." This is a subjective selection, as compared to the objective measurement used by Cattell.

The weakness of the objective method is revealed in the list. Among the first hundred eminent persons of the world's history, Cattell found one woman. She was not Cleopatra or Catherine of Russia or Elizabeth I of England or Joan of Arc. She was Mary, Queen of Scots. The reason for her unexpected, and undeserved, place near the top of the list is that more than one nation was involved in Mary's love affairs, plots, controversies, and tragedy, so that her biography appears at some length in encyclopedias written in different countries and languages.

With the top hundred from Cattell and another top hundred from Ruoff, I was able to make the list even shorter and more manageable. Forty-nine names appear on both lists, indicating that they have survived the test of both objective and subjective selection.

One of them, Homer, is a shadowy figure at the most and may never have lived as the sole author of the epic poems which bear his name. We know nothing about him. "He is," says one encylopedia, "nothing but the author of the Homeric Poems," and he may not have been even that.

Of the remaining forty-eight, though with some overlapping, eight were military men who possessed some quality of statesmanship, four were religious leaders, and twelve were writers.

* Edited by Henry W. Ruoff, published by The Frontier Press, Buffalo, N.Y., 1910.

The many-sided Benjamin Franklin could be listed in several categories. There are a number of philosophers among the forty-eight who were also scientists, writers, astronomers, or even poets. Evidently, there is no particular pattern that applies to greatness, nor is there any employment that contributes much to it, though the power of the pen and the sword is indicated by the relatively large enrollment of soldiers and writers. Incidentally, five of the forty-eight died violent deaths.

All these forty-eight had personalities which were out in the open. In one way or another, their lives were made public. Their virtues and vices were put on record, often by prejudiced persons, but often truthfully. A glance at the first ten names on the list, which is here arranged according to Cattell's estimate of their importance, reveals that none of them could be omitted from any catalogue of the world's great men. It will also be noted that nobody born after the year 1809 is listed among the forty-eight.

The first ten, in the order of their alleged or estimated importance, are:

Napoleon I	Aristotle
Shakespeare	Goethe
Mohammed	Julius Caesar
Voltaire	Martin Luther
Francis Bacon	Plato

Napoleon and Julius Caesar hammered their way to the top as military leaders but supported their conquests with considerable statesmanship. Both, however, let their vanity overcome their intellects and, in different ways, destroyed themselves. It is curious that both are said to have had lapses of consciousness. In Shakespeare's phrase, Julius Caesar had the "falling sickness," which may have been epilepsy, but not necessarily so. His greatness is not easy to understand, for he was one of many able, ambitious, and ruthless men of his time who might have matched his achievements except for the fortunes of war. A defeated

soldier, in those days, rarely lived to fight again, and his con-
queror usually took care that he did not. So Caesar "bestrode the
narrow world" for a while above the corpses of those who had
challenged him, and died at last at the hands of others who in
their turn would die suddenly.

The story of Napoleon is less puzzling, but again circumstances
have much to do with his greatness in the eyes of the encyclo-
pedists and the hearts of his countrymen. Jacques Bainville said
of him, "If he had died a natural death in his palace, or fallen on
the field of battle, Napoleon would never have become to poster-
ity the figure we know." But we would have known, perhaps,
that inordinate vanity and arrogance took possession of him
in his time of triumph, wrecking him as mental disease may ruin
the lives of lesser men.

Books about Napoleon are still coming off the presses. In the
literary section of the New York *Times* of April 29, 1956, is a
review of such a book, which reminds us that many patients in
mental hospitals have called themselves "Napoleons." But Napoleon himself was a dreamer. "As a youth he imagined himself
to be Napoleon—and later he was!"

Two others of the ten were religious leaders, both remarkable
men who are reported to have suffered lapses of consciousness.
Were they trances or hallucinations? The evidence is obscured
by the devotion of their followers, but there was genius in both
Mohammed and Martin Luther, as far apart as the poles in their
lives and convictions.

Of the two Greek philosophers who command top honors
in the list, Plato is known to have shown at times an intense
melancholy resembling that of the mental patient. This does
not, of course, dispute his greatness, nor the enormous effect
of the teachings of both Plato and Aristotle on the minds and
history of man.

Among the ten we also find two men with great character
defects. Francis Bacon was a pioneer of modern science and
philosophy, but he was also a man who taught morals while he

took bribes and prosecuted the Earl of Essex, who had befriended him. Yet, if we are honest with ourselves, we may find in our hearts a fellow feeling for the man who was "the wisest, brightest, meanest of mankind," a paradox of unreconciled motives and emotions.

Voltaire was a superb literary craftsman, a defender of the oppressed; but he was also vain, unscrupulous, without dignity, jealous, and greedy. He railed and sulked in his room for a whole day because his host's servant misplaced his cup at the breakfast table. He lived to a triumphant old age, as if to spite his many enemies, but no student of his life could possibly mistake him for a normal man. Does it now begin to appear why I say that geniuses are really closer to mental patients than they are to me?

A pleasant ending to the ten men "most written-about-in-encyclopedias" comes with Goethe and Shakespeare. Goethe, the greatest German poet, was stable in spite of a tremendous imagination and a stormy adolescence—a universal genius, a mystic, botanist, biologist, lawyer, statesman, with some medical training. From his writings I select a sentence which might be written above the door of a mental hospital: "If you inquire what the people are like here, I must answer, 'The same as everywhere!'" And inside the door might be written on the wall his belief that: "One ought, every day at least, to hear a little song, read a good poem, see a fine picture, and, if it were possible, to speak a few reasonable words."

Shakespeare's greatness is undisputed, except by those who believe that somebody else wrote his plays and poetry. It seems to me that they have overlooked the best argument to support their position, though their evident weakness is that they do not agree on the same candidate for Shakespeare's place of honor. His plays are marked by perfect dramatic instinct and penetrating understanding; they are written with "complete imagination"; they are "capricious and unsystematic," to the delight of the world. Yet there is virtually nothing in the prosaic, sensible, businesslike life of their author, as we know of it, to suggest his genius.

The second ten in the gallery of greatness are:

Homer	Washington
Newton	Raphael
Cicero	Descartes
Milton	Columbus
Alexander	Confucius

Here again are the familiar figures of the soldier, statesman, philosopher, and poet, but the explorer and artist appear for the first time. It is sufficient to say of these ten that if greatness or genius is anything, it is also everything.

The third ten are an even more varied lot. Here we have:

Sir Walter Scott	Kant
Michelangelo	Leibnitz
Socrates	Locke
Oliver Cromwell	Demosthenes
Guatama (Buddha)	Calvin

The psychoses of old age came at last to Sir Walter Scott and to Immanuel Kant. With Scott, there was a happy outcome—the loss of memory to which I alluded earlier. Working desperately to pay off a mountain of debt which had been placed upon him by an innocent and foolish venture in a publishing house, he had a stroke and then a progressive loss of memory. When this had advanced far enough, he began to believe that all his debts had been paid, and this delusion made his last years happy.

In the case of Kant, there was the same story of stroke and memory loss, but not such a happy ending—only confusion.

The fourth group of ten contains names of several men who could challenge their competitors for higher places on the list if they were not evaluated by encyclopedia linage. They are:

Moliere	Frederick the Great
Lincoln	Hegel
Dante	Charles V
Franklin	Virgil
Galileo	Hume

The last nine of the forty-nine are Gibbon, Wordsworth, Admiral Nelson, Schiller, Jefferson, Leonardo da Vinci, Rubens, Mozart, and Cuvier, the French naturalist.

I want to try to place some of these men on this very exclusive list in their approximate places on our scale of the normal, more or less. When I looked for the most normal among the great I found it safest to consider first the three founding fathers of the United States.

It is something of a shock to realize that Washington was probably the least gifted and most normal of all these great men. He was sound in judgment, steady, controlled, calm, and brave, but not brilliant. Close to Washington was Jefferson, who had a "smattering of knowledge about a great many things," who was gay and quick, tactful, a gifted politician and writer. The third American, Franklin, was certainly more brilliant than Washington or Jefferson, yet he is the world's example of a practical man, wise, clever, kind, and sometimes deceitful in a good cause. There was in these three men no suggestion of the precocious genius which showed in Mozart, Michelangelo, and others at the ages of four or five.

What we know about the following five men puts them high on our scale: Aristotle; Demosthenes; John Locke, lofty, patient, tolerant, with unsullied integrity and with friendliness; Schiller, "the best of friends, the best of fathers, the best of husbands"; and Virgil, whom Dante chose as his "Dear Guide and Wisdom" on his journey through hell. I add Mozart to this splendid group because his one honorable vice, inability to handle money, was offset by the cruel treatment visited on him by those who handled money too well. He was delicate, childlike, generous, and sympathetic; a lofty musician of musicians, "the greatest genius in the whole history of music."

Lower on the scale are Gibbon and Hume, who carried violent prejudices over into their histories. Hume became a hypochondriac at twenty-three. Frederick the Great was, on one side, dirty, cruel, harsh, and brutal; but, on another side, he was "the most conspicuous and enlightened ruler of his time."

As we approach the subject of depressions in great men we have to keep in mind, as always, that these are interruptions in men's lives. Newton's nervousness, insomnia, and worries, and Wordsworth's moral dejection and doubts seem to be neuroses on the edge of depression. So also with Cromwell's "religious depressions" and "searing convictions of sin," and Descartes' dark moods of solitary brooding.

But Abraham Lincoln had a full depressed state. In Hapgood's description,* "Lincoln, tending toward fits of gloom, had his mind almost shattered by the blow. . . . He and his friends feared for his sanity. . . . He was so overcome by depression, whenever he was alone, that he no longer dared to carry a pocketknife. . . . If the great President is ever to be understood as a man, it must be by reconciling wonderful sanity with vagaries almost insane. . . . He wrote his partner: 'I am now the most miserable man living. If what I feel were equally distributed to the whole human family, there would not be one cheerful face on earth. Whether I shall be better I cannot tell: I awfully forbode I shall not.' "

This discussion of great men is sketchy, and I have deliberately not considered persons where interpretation was difficult, sometimes impossible. I hope that some readers will build up another list of people who have lived in the first half of this century and who may be considered great or encyclopedia-worthy in the year 2050. Up for study would come Schweitzer, Fleming, Fermi, Ford, Einstein, Freud, Hitler, Lenin, Winston Churchill, F. D. Roosevelt, Marconi, Edison, Proust, Picasso, Woodrow Wilson,

* Norman Hapgood, *Abraham Lincoln*. The Macmillan Company, New York, 1899.

Gandhi. Probably not all of these, perhaps not many, will be considered normal in the longer perspective of history.

If we turn away from the arbitrary list of the forty-nine "greatest" of the past, we can easily find clear-cut examples of gradations of normality, arranged more or less in accordance with our familiar line. At the top might be Emerson, friendly neighbor, practical poet and optimist, serene and sweet-tempered philosopher.

Charles Dickens could stand for the almost-normal man with one besetting weakness, his sense of insecurity. Tennyson, whom we have discussed before, suffered from dark, brooding moods which deeply disturbed his private life, though they appear rarely, if at all, in his writings. Richard Wagner was neurotic, paranoid, and his violent mental life had much to do with his music.

Samuel Coleridge, a great poet, was a drug addict. Robert Burns was an alcoholic, a victim of profound depressions. Edgar Allan Poe was morbid and an alcoholic. Vincent Van Gogh, high on the list as an artist, was schizophrenic.

And so, like characters in books, novels, and biographies, like people met in medical practice, great men fall into line and are not by any means clustered at the top of the scale of normality. No matter how much ability a person has, or how famous and powerful he is, he shares the problem of us all. He is "part of the human predicament"; he has to manage himself and he becomes a tragic figure if he cannot do so.

A man of great genius has an even harder time in managing himself than an average person. If his emotional development, his "character," his relationships with other people do not keep up with his great gift, he is in trouble. Therefore, the closest to a common denominator among forty-nine or a hundred or a thousand great men is not found in their triumphs, but in their troubles—the troubles which, in some degree, we share with them.

Chapter VII

MENTAL HEALTH
IN THE FAMILY

I CANNOT contribute much to the study of heredity; I do not know exactly what it is. But I have seen three or four generations of many families and from them have learned to respect the idea that heredity consists of our getting from our parents certain genes—elements in a fertilized cell which give us our native equipment—and also a certain environment. Besides eye and skin color and musical and other abilities, we inherit a certain place and station in life for our developing years. It may be in a slum, on a farm, in a large or small family, with much or little education in the people about us. In a sense we even inherit the brothers and sisters who come after us, for we live with them during our most impressionable years and they are part of our intimate environment.

By observing the families whom I have known, I have come to believe that a single case of mental disease need not have much meaning for family members of the next generation. Where many similar cases pile up "unto the third or fourth generation," there is a serious effect on descendants. An amazing family, of which I knew one member, consisted of parents who both had similar depressions and exhilarations, and also nine children, of whom the first eight had similar illnesses; only one, the youngest, escaped. An opposite situation was that of two parents, both psychiatrists, whose daughter became schizophrenic. This girl, at the age of twenty-two, was afraid to go to the bathroom in a hospital in Philadelphia because she thought her father, who lived in New York, would be hiding there to rape her. The parents, whose families had been in this country since colonial times, were determined to find some evidence of mental trouble in their ancestors, but they could find none; the well-documented families had a clean bill of health.

So now as always, I turn to books* and to articles by Franz J. Kallmann, who is entitled to his opinions—and they are not simple. He arrived at them by using painstaking methods of control in the examination of identical and dissimilar twins. Then he went further and studied the brothers and sisters of thousands of patients with a severe mental disease. His opinion that there is a "hereditary inadequacy of certain tissues" in certain mental patients who retire from real life into their own world is solidly founded. Many physicians guess that this idea can be spread over many men and women who suffer from the minor ills that "flesh is heir to."

From my own files, I can offer accounts of whole families who can be placed on our scale of normality as if they were individuals. Here, first, is a story to gladden a psychiatrist's heart —a story of happiness, ease, and success.

On the mother's side is a grandfather who is a judge, warm and strong, and a grandmother who is optimistic, sociable, poised, devoted to her husband and her children. The mother is frank, outgoing, responsible, and was president of her class in college. Like the father, she delighted in encouraging any step toward independence that her children made.

On the father's side is a notably strong and serene grandfather and a loving and spirited grandmother. They had seven children, all happy and successful, and they "enjoyed their children." The father cannot understand why people talk so often about unhappiness in childhood and in adolescence. All his memories of growing up are pleasant ones. He is a successful trust officer with many

* Franz J. Kallmann, *Genetics of Schizophrenia.* J. J. Augustin, Inc., Publisher, New York, 1938.

friends, and he is conscientious and responsible, with great affection for his home and family.

From these antecedents comes a son who was shy as a boy but became president of his college class, served easily and well in the Air Force, made a happy marriage, and keeps his love for his parents. A daughter has just graduated from college, where she was president of her class, friendly to men, women, and children, forceful, humorous, efficient, and responsible.

Every marriage in this family has been long-lasting and deeply satisfying.

A second family shows a paternal grandfather who was a quiet, sincere, efficient minister. His wife was well balanced, full of energy, and well liked by her husband's congregations. The maternal grandfather was president of an Eastern university, a fine teacher who worked too hard and had a "nervous break-down." His wife was quiet and unselfish.

The middle generation in this case is really remarkable. There was a very happy marriage between the father and the mother. The father was "well balanced, an outstanding athlete, a musi-cian, conscientious, fair, reliable," well liked and active in civic affairs, a professor in college. His oldest sister, also married, is capable, charming, even-tempered, steady, likeable. A second sister is an unusual person with many interests, "a teacher who has a wonderful way with children"; she is restless, nervous, strong, kind, and generous. A brother is an able administrator, an outdoors man (in forestry service) who has lots of drive and is well liked.

Now for a look at the mother's side. The mother herself is a good manager, artistic, and generous. As with the rest of her family, "money did not mean much" to her. Perhaps this partly accounts for the fact that her two sisters and three brothers took advanced degrees. The men became highly competent college professors, while the women occupy important teaching positions and are "sensible and charming, friendly and outgoing."

In the third generation there are two daughters. One, only

fifteen, is somewhat oppressed by her teachers' desire—and perhaps her parents'—that she keep up to the family's high academic standards. The other, twenty-one, is a well-balanced scholar, cook, musician, and leader, but not as much at ease as she should be.

Of the two families mentioned so far, the first has created character—as all families should. The second is also constructive, but with more friction along the way.

Now we come to three families, their histories as uniform as the others, where character seems to have been warped and destroyed instead of created.

In the first of the three, the grandparents could hardly have been more different from those in our first two families. The father's father, in Poland, was a rigid, arbitrary man who allowed his wife to say only a few words in a month. She almost forgot how to talk. The mother's father, in the United States, was able in business but irascible at home, and his wife talked more than most women. The household echoed with their quarrels.

In the second generation we find the father a rigid perfectionist, a successful man who expected his wife and children to take his orders. The wife fought him every inch of the way and was bitter and unhappy.

Three sons born from this marriage became, respectively, an alcoholic, a schizophrenic, and a hobo, as if each had found his own way out of an intolerable predicament.

Tension seems to go from father to son in the second of our three less fortunate families.

The grandfather "should have died early," it was said; he was opinionated and unfair and carried on a constant battle—"with terrific tensions"—with his wife.

The father had hated his own father, but he idolized his own son. He had heard "enough arguments between my parents so that I want none now." To bring about this peace, he became a dictator, telling his son that "if you love me, you will do as I say." He was rigid and always unhappy.

The son raised under this domination is now twenty-two, but he has not grown up. He depends on his mother for support, is overweight and overfed, and is a sissy, afraid of any responsibility.

Here is a brief outline of the third unhappy family group.

A great-grandmother was completely selfish, dominating her only daughter. A grandmother was tense, afraid to leave home, overprotecting her only daughter.

A mother, in the third generation, is afraid to travel in buses or trains; she constantly and alternately cuddles and rages at her only daughter.

The daughter is already neurotic at the age of six. Is she ready to repeat the same miserable story? And can we say with any assurance how much of the little girl's character and condition is due to her native equipment—her genes—and how much is due to the persistent environment of selfishness, tension, and destructive dominance that have haunted the household for half a century or more? We may say cautiously that there is a bent, or tendency, that has been passed along from mother to daughter for four generations, but we may not say that inexorable and ineluctable fate has laid the same burden on them all in turn. Somewhere along the line there could have been escape from the curse and a change for the better in a better environment. If we do not believe that, what have we left of human freedom?

We are likely to look upon the mid-Victorian family as something out-of-date, found only in novels and plays. It is true that nowadays it does not meet with open approval, and fathers today do not have the financial hold on sons and daughters that was dramatized in *The Barretts of Wimpole Street*. Nevertheless, some of its worst aspects survive, insidiously and under cover. What these are is shown brilliantly in *The Way of All Flesh*, written by Samuel Butler in the years between 1873 and 1885, about the Pontifex family.*

* This novel was published in 1903, one year after the author's death. It is largely autobiographical, and the characters are mostly taken, with changes, from real life. (*Encyclopaedia Brittanica*, Vol. 4, p. 465, 1952.)

George Pontifex, the grandfather, advanced himself in the world and married a lady who brought a good dowry and died after the birth of a fifth child. He was a stern man who thrashed his two boys twice a week whether they deserved it or not. "It was hard for a man so fond of money to be fond of children, too." He was also a hypocrite who forced his son Theobald into the ministry, ignoring the boy's real abilities and overriding his objections.

The other grandparents, the Allabys, had a tiny income, two sons, and seven daughters. Mrs. Allaby spent her life scheming to marry off the daughters (one cannot blame her for that!), and, after four years' work, she saw her daughter Christina married to Theobald Pontifex.

Theobald lost no time in showing Christina that he was master of the house, and after that he received her loyal collaboration. As a minister, he was completely assured of his own virtue and believed that there "were no good people who did not think as he did." Of his children he expected adult behavior; if he did not get it, he thrashed them. He could not conceive that any reasonable person could have wants which would inconvenience him or his wife. Sadly the author comments that "one great reason why clergymen's households are generally unhappy is because the clergyman is so much at home and close around the house," and "the clergymen's children are the most defenseless things within reach."

Now for his wife, Christina. "If it was not such an awful thing to say of anyone, I should say that she meant well." Originally kindly, "she might have been all right if she had married a sensible inn-keeper." But, swayed by her husband, she used love and humility to ride roughshod over her children; to drag out of them every private thought to report to their father; to invade any privacy of mind; to interfere with any friendships. In a letter to her sons she implored them to be "obedient, affectionate, attentive to their father's wishes, self-denying and diligent"—which Butler describes as the behavior most convenient to parents.

Then there were the three children of Theobald and Christina, and again we have arrived at the third generation. Of them, Joseph is not described at all, Charlotte is dismissed as "an odious young woman," and Ernest becomes the focus of attention. Bullied by his father, wheedled by his mother, loved and spoiled by an aunt, he is a mixed-up child, a foolish, idle, listless boy at school. He finds himself as a man only after he discovers that his father and mother are his most deadly enemies.

Alfred Lord Tennyson, who was almost "Mr. Victorian Age," had an astonishing family history. About his maternal grandparents, a rector and a niece of the Bishop of London, little is said. But his paternal grandmother, Mary, was religious to an extreme, affectionate, musical, and a minor poet. Her husband had no religion; he was domineering, irritable, and at times depressed, often violent and sarcastic.

Tennyson's mother was an angelic beauty, pious and simple. Her relationship to her husband became "horrible" as twelve children came along. And Tennyson's father—a rector who, like Theobald Pontifex, disliked church but was forced into his position by his nonreligious father—was always irritable, often depressed and confused, and an alcoholic. He was sharp and severe with his family and punished the children for his own imperfections. But he had a real devotion to good literature; he made Alfred learn by heart four books of Horace before he was seven years old!

Of Alfred's eight brothers, the first died in infancy, the second had depressions and took to opium, the third had a chronic mental disease. The fourth was Alfred, who in early life had "blackblooded depressions." The fifth is unaccounted for, the sixth had depressions and was an alcoholic, the seventh was erratic (probably an understatement), and the eighth had depressions. The four sisters who came at the end of the line were apparently normal. Alfred went through a cruel school which he hated. All this as background and preparation for a successful Poet Laureate! I should hate to be sentenced to read all his works, but his lyrics in *The Princess, Ulysses,* and some verses from *In Memoriam* seem to be lasting gifts to literature.

Much to the point is the family history of George du Maurier, because the record of his happiness and success in marriage, as an illustrator, and as an author is as clear as it is outstanding.*

The maternal grandmother, Mary Anne, was an aspiring courtesan who sparked the liveliest scandal ever to rock the House of Commons. She lived by her wits—charming, clever, ruthless—and the best that could be said of her was that she was a good fighter. Who the maternal grandfather was no one ever knew—"king or dustman."

Du Maurier's mother was dragged all over Europe, always lonely and insecure. A worse upbringing can hardly be imagined; even a settled way of life in a slum might be better for a growing girl. As she grew older she longed for respectability. Although usually quiet, she had a touchy temper and was a good fighter.

The paternal grandparents had pretensions to aristocracy but had lost their properties in France—exiled to England, the grandfather tried to support a large family by teaching school. All the family members were gentle and appreciative of the finer things in life. The father of George du Maurier shocked this respectable family by studying opera and becoming a singer in second-rate companies touring the provinces—he was careless, generous, always in debt, lazy and unreliable—always trying to invent something that would bring in a fortune. He died, singing, at fifty-nine.

Here we certainly have an extraordinary family history and background for genius. Yet du Maurier himself was a sunny, silent, obedient baby and a music-loving, dreamy, sensitive child. He was inattentive at school and did not want to grow up. Although he wished to become an artist, his father forced him to become a chemist and, after he failed college entrance examinations, to open a chemistry laboratory in London. At twenty-one he was frustrated by falling in love with his aunt. Then, at twenty-two, the death of his father allowed him to go to Paris to

* Daphne du Maurier, The Du Mauriers, Doubleday Doran & Co., New York, 1937. See also Mary Anne by the same author, published by Doubleday Doran & Co., 1954. (The first book is a biography of the Du Maurier family; the second, a fictional version of the life of her great-great-grandmother.)

study art; his happy, impoverished days there are reflected in his novel *Trilby*. At twenty-five he lost one eye and the other was threatened; in his despair he planned suicide, but he was reassured about total loss of eyesight. He was married at twenty-nine. From that time on he displayed the great concentration and determination which helped to bring him long happiness and success in art, in literature, and in family life.

Daphne du Maurier, his gifted granddaughter, believes that George inherited his artistic abilities from his father's side but inherited his fighting spirit, his will to succeed, from his mother's mother who "rose to the pinnacle of trollopdom."

After considering his family record, I am happy to repeat that I don't know much about heredity. And I wonder if anybody does. Several theories of heredity have been worked out fairly well with fruit flies, rats, and white mice; but here we are dealing with human beings.

Now to go back to some mixed histories of people I know. One family is distinguished through several generations by the strength of character found in its women.

The paternal grandfather was a mild man, well liked, who was never able to do well in business. His wife was the "ruler of the family," capable, stubborn, and determined. The maternal grandfather was warm and friendly, original, unconventional, and ineffective. His wife was a "matriarch, if ever there was one."

The father was a poor fit in business, "nervous," warm, generous. His wife was a "born businesswoman" who "made things hum."

In the third generation were two sons and two daughters. The first son was soon and easily discouraged by any difficulty; he was vacillating and subject to mild depressive swings. The second son was artistic, ineffective, but likeable. The first daughter was a good manager, realistic, and rather cold; the second had a "fine, free, flexible mind" capable of dealing with any situation. There is logic in this series of symptoms—if we can find it.

In the next family, I am interested in the traits which made most impression on succeeding generations. I doubt that it is good to be remembered for abstinence, which is a negative thing. The ministry and teaching can be "censorious professions," and many of its representatives practice what they preach both on themselves and their families.

The great-grandparents were all meticulous and set in their views. They used no alcohol or tobacco. Both great-grandfathers were ministers, good preachers but hard taskmasters. The grand-parents were teachers, strong, strict, "W.C.T.U. and all that."

In the third generation is a strict mother, prim and overcon-scientious, and a father who is a rebel, an anarchist who hates religion.

In the fourth generation are two children—a girl who is a perfectionist and frustrated, and a boy who doesn't care about anything.

So much for three-generation families. I now want to turn to some sets of parents, pivotal members of the family, as they have been described by their children. Because Philip Wylie and Dr. Edward Strecker have reported on the "Great American Mom," I want first to report on the "Great American Pop," the seamy side of a minority of fathers, and then come to the "Moms." No "Pop" or "Mom" has a high place in the line of normality. They are described here because there are enough of them to produce a large amount of unhappiness, and because they remind me of the Pontifexes in Butler's novel.

Here are typical remarks made by troubled sons and a daughter about their respective fathers.

"Father won't allow any mental disease in our family."

"Father is the headmaster of a boys' school. He has never been known to praise anyone, but he never fails to notice every mis-take. He is a grand critic."

"When father loses at checkers to my little sister, he bangs the board down on the floor."

"Father whistles for mother when he wants her to come running."

"My grandfather was a shipbuilder and tried to make my father into one. Father broke away after a bitter struggle and became a musician. Then I came along, and father was all set on my taking music lessons and doing all the things he had not been able to do as a boy. I hated music, and I had to have a fight with father to break away and get a chance to build boats."

"Father says he will break every bone in my body if I study music, which is the only thing I want to do."

"I worshiped father; I was an adoring daughter. At fourteen he told me about all he had to stand from mother, and I was on his side. Father kept me from boys, but I didn't mind. I kept thinking I would like to be great like my father. But at twenty, when I was at college, I began to see my father as a spoiled child. He could not delegate anything. He was fantastically busy, never at home, and mother was starved for interest and attention in a little town. Now I have moved out from his shadow, and I am growing up, but last month I broke under the strain. I'm better now."

Here are some things which fathers, proudly holding their positions as "heads of families," voting citizens, and respectable neighbors, have told me they "didn't believe in":

heredity   poor people
pediatrics   psychiatry
sex   newspapers
democracy   growing old
politeness   cancer
hospitals   psychology
happiness   the abnormal
modern ideas   poetry
fiction   fat or pregnant women
girls with bands on their teeth

The "Moms" do not present a pleasing picture, either, in the eyes and words of their disturbed children.

"Mother scolded me for hours because I got in at 10:30 last night. She doesn't know that I am forty years old. I wish I understood mother love, and I wish she was someone else's mother!"

"Mother punishes people by not speaking to them for years at a time."

"Mother knows all the answers. She dominates father and me by sweetness and heart attacks."

Another "Mom" type of mother lived in an apartment which commanded a view of her married son's front porch. Every trip made by her son or daughter-in-law had to be explained to her. Where did they go? When would they be back? The couple, about forty years old, had an ingenious method of getting around this inspection. They would leave the car standing on a side street on a downgrade, then creep out of a back door and let the car coast for a block before turning on the ignition.

Here are more "Moms" who won't or can't leave their sons alone.

"Mother wept and wailed when I got engaged. She said that Ellen could never love me as she did. When Ellen and I were away mother rearranged all our furniture."

"Mother is the religious leader of her community. She has never read a disagreeable book or faced a disagreeable fact in her life."

In the field of the family, there remain husbands and wives who, of course, may also be fathers and mothers. Often when they try to describe each other, they describe themselves. Again they illustrate the destructive forces in marriage, and again it is not so much the unhappiness they reveal in themselves as the thought of how much misery they will hand down to new generations that is distressing.

"Husbands," said one woman, "are good to cut the grass and take the children to the movies, and that's all."

Another told me, "My husband is so decent, so refined, and so good to his mother that I can't stand him."

Another gives the same idea a different twist. "My husband

is so wonderful that I can't love him." But here is a more spiteful statement: "I am filled with pure hate of my husband, and he pays no attention. I call him Mr. God."

In many ways and different words husbands and wives reveal the tensions which make marriages hell rather than heaven.

"I've always danced around the edge of my husband's moods."

"I don't like my husband, I don't like myself, and, you know, I never did like the Lord."

"My husband weeps for his mother every night."

"For my wife I never had an inside feeling—I have a feeling toward blonds."

"My beautiful wife did not believe in sex. She had a passion for dogs. We lived on a desolate hill. We had the only house, and the winds whined and howled about it. All around were the graves of dogs; it looked like a cemetery for children. The colored couple who looked after us used to see ghosts. It was kind of gloomy."

Here is another story of tangled web of misery in matrimony, told to me by a man who evidently thought the fault lay altogether on the distaff side of his household.

"You see, the day before Christmas I left the office after a hard day; I met a friend, and over a drink I tried to get his ideas about business. Then three men came along who might have valuable information, and we had a few drinks. I telephoned home that I would arrive at nine, and at ten I got there in a pouring rain and found my wife and son. I said to them, 'This shouldn't happen to a dog.' The kids were making a racket, and I jumped on them and then on my wife, who was raising her voice. From eleven to 4:30 A.M. I got a curtain lecture, and my wife would shake me awake every time I dozed off. She had baked a wonderful cake for me, and I hadn't tasted it. On Christmas Day I sort of accidentally hit her, and my wife left me." A merry Christmas, indeed!

The psychiatrist is concerned with a man who celebrates Christmas by drinking too much, getting delusions of self-importance, blaming his weaknesses on somebody else, losing his temper, and beating his wife—and then can't imagine how or why it all happened!

The great migration to the suburbs in modern times, brought to light in the 1950 census, makes the position of the suburban family in the line-up more important than it used to be. There are many more of them, and they have more than average influence. Here are six well-to-do and intelligent members of a pleasant community several miles out of Boston.

Mr. A. gets on very well in business. "I like people, and people like me. I like lots of human sympathy, and unfortunately I don't get it from my wife. She doesn't understand me." Mrs. A. meets her husband's adolescence by saying, "It is lucky for me that I have a fine father. He doesn't approve of all these new ideas, and I don't either. It is wonderful to have father's help, and I hope to bring up my boy to be just like him." Her thinking does not include the intermediate masculine generation, which is her husband, but she works hard and is a good housekeeper.

Mr. B. is a brilliant inventor. He is aggressive in his laboratory, but at home he is passive, gentle, unromantic. "I leave everything to my wife," he tells me. The wife, Mrs. B., is an exponent of "the new freedom." "I am carrying on an affair with Mr. A., and I don't care who knows it. Anyway, I tell my husband all about it, and he is sympathetic. Of course, my husband is just a brain. My parents were mid-Victorian; thank heaven I rebelled."

Mr. C. is a hard-working supervisor in a manufacturing plant. He is an "incoming husband" who wants to read the newspapers and the scientific journals in the evenings. "That's all—I have no use for parties or movies." But Mrs. C. is an "outgoing wife," active in all community affairs, "ready to burst" at her husband's dullness and seclusiveness, angry at him partly because "I have always had the worst of everything, ever since my sister got out of all the work and loaded it on me."

These people are profoundly unhappy, of course, and may

become more so unless they pull themselves together, face realities, and discard their adolescent or self-indulgent attitudes.

I repeat that these are true stories of real people. Although I am
confident that no individual cited in this book will be identified,
my friends have thought they recognized these suburbanites as
their neighbors in Cambridge, Mass.; Haddonfield, N. J.;
Swarthmore, Pa.; and Stamford, Conn. If someone ever reads
this book in a suburb of San Francisco, this typical suburban
group will be located there, too. No matter where you are in
the United States, if you want to see the groups or individuals
I have described—look about you.

In the fact that the family can create character or warp or ruin
it lies hope and tragedy. I came across this dramatic true story
on a visit to an old college friend in California, who knew that
the "hero" of this tale had been a friend of mine.

George Chumley, as we shall call him, had an established
position in Boston; he was a member of one of the city's old
families and the devoted son of his mother. His father died when
George was eight, and it was natural that his mother should
turn her full affections to him, her only child. Up to the time
he was forty his mother kept house for him, saw to it that he
did not get married, and had him as escort for evening events
and as a companion on vacations.

When he was forty-one some men persuaded him to join
them on a fishing trip with a guide, but no women. He announced
this plan to his mother. She rose from her chair, her face flushed,
her eyes glaring, her anger so intense that she could not speak
but could only pound the floor with her cane. He thought she
was going to strike him, but then she fell dead at his feet. And
George laughed—and found that he could not stop laughing.
Minutes went by; his laughter could not be controlled. He
thought he ought to call a doctor and reached for the telephone,
but stopped when he realized that he could not let the operator
hear him, nor could he tell the doctor what had happened amid
peals of laughter. Fifteen minutes later he was at last able to

put the call through in what, he congratulated himself, was the correct manner.

I cannot leave the subject of the family without repeating some of the ideas of Porter Lee * and Prentice Murphy concerning its constructive, creative power. They see the family as a small group which can provide intimacy, security, and fellowship for its members of different ages, and so give them strength to meet an outside world "of strangers and dangers." In the family there can be wise use of promotion—the first allowance, the first party dress, the first time a child is allowed to stay up until nine in the evening, the first responsible errand. There can be opportunity for privacy, a shelf or bureau drawer of one's own which nobody else is allowed to touch, and perhaps a room of one's own. There can be festivals, birthday parties, graduations, holidays; there can be family rejoicing over advancements and good fortune. There can also be considerate and understanding appraisal of failures and forgiveness for errors.

Prentice Murphy † warns of one mistake often made in family life. That is the expectation or assumption that any individual remains always at a constant level. "The lover," he points out, "does not always love; the believer does not always believe; the doubter does not always doubt. . . . Devotion and interest are constantly shifting."

"The lover does not always love." Sometimes he or she is too tired or too sleepy. Sometimes a man or woman discovers new objectives and occasions for affection. With the passing years parents may outgrow the emotion that first brought them together, yet still be much in love. Such changes in devotion allow and encourage a full development of the individual and the possibility of a fuller response. Children of such parents are also growing; they respond by instinct and imitation to the increasing maturity of their father and mother.

* Porter R. Lee and others, *Mental Hygiene and Social Work*. Commonwealth Fund, New York, 1929.
† Pamphlets issued by the School of Social Work, Philadelphia.

Chapter VIII

THE ELUSIVE NORMAL

An effort to find a definition, or at least a description, of the normal, a term frequently used in former chapters, calls for both a direct and indirect approach.

About a dozen years ago I tried a direct way. I knew that physicians in general and psychiatrists in particular had been getting their ideas about human nature from observation of people who selected themselves, or were selected by others, because they were in trouble. And I knew that people who are not in trouble do not as a rule want to be studied; they are too busy or impatient or they want to leave well enough alone. But if you assume that health is simply the absence of disease, you are leaving out something vital.

Dr. Arlie Bock, of the Harvard Student Health Service, had let me help in the Grant study.* This was a thorough investigation and follow-up of students chosen because they were doing well in the sophomore year at college. It included physical and psychological examinations, fatigue tests, and visits by a social worker to the students' homes. This was a fascinating project, and its full values and accomplishments are yet to be recorded.

This Harvard experiment was too large for me to repeat, and I wanted a more objective method of selection, including women as well as men. I was near Bryn Mawr, Haverford, and Swarthmore Colleges—respectively for women, men, and coeducational —and knew that their admissions were carefully selected. I supposed, rightly, that they had student councils, and I asked the

---

* C. W. Heath et al., *What People Are*. Harvard University Press, Cambridge, 1946; and many other reports.

members of these councils to volunteer for a study; only one person stayed out. Sixty-four came in to meet a psychiatrist for several hours, to take Rorschach and Thematic Apperception procedures, and to prepare their families for a visit from a social worker. The results of physical examinations and student aptitude tests were available.

Here was a group chosen by two selections with which the examiners had nothing to do—regular college admissions and a certain amount of college success. One college president told me, "It is as normal a group as you'll ever get."

The obstacles in the way of finding a better group seem almost insurmountable. It is suggested that this group is overweighted in intelligence. It is. But when I think of the ways in which the study was helped by the intelligence of the students and their parents, I feel that it would be too difficult to explain to citizens taken at random the purpose of the undertaking and reasons why they should cooperate.

The advantages of the council group became more apparent as the work went on. Arrangements for appointments could be made and discussed at regular council meetings. The ages of the students meant that parents were thinking of their children as independent persons removed from the family setting, and yet were able to remember the important events of the students' earlier years. Also the parents could give a good account of their own parents and brothers and sisters, and so make a three-generation study.

Now these sixty-four students, chosen simply as representatives of their classmates, divided themselves into four groups.*

1. A group of women for whom some of the Rorschach words are "good mind, lively imagination, rare, exquisite, creative, excellent potential," while the psychiatrists' words are "loyal, altruistic, good citizen." In these women there is at most a slight moodiness, and in some a proper hostility.

* E. D. Bond, "The Student Council Study, An Approach to the Normal," *American Journal of Psychiatry*, Vol. 109, pp. 11–16, (July) 1952.

The corresponding group of men contains several older than the average because of military service, in which they had showed courage and stability under stress. Words in the Rorschachs are "good inner resources, good minds, rich and vigorous, clear and orderly thinking, strong and spontaneous instincts." Words from the psychiatrists' interviews are "friendly, steady, idealistic, handles people well." In these men can be seen slight hostilities and slight depressive tendencies.

In this total group, liabilities appear completely overwhelmed by assets.

2. A group where the women are described as "warm, attractive, conforming, realistic, modest with mild drives, sensuous, amiable," while the men's abilities and ambitions are modest. All are steady and well adjusted and show only the very slightest signs of uneasiness.

There are a very few men who seem extremely well balanced on a very low level; that is, they are commonplace, shallow, smooth, successful.

3. About a fourth of all the sixty-four students have in common extraordinary abilities and important neurotic traits. Descriptions of the women carry the words "richly creative, popular, altruistic, attractive, charming, clear, artistic." The men are described as "excellent in inner resources, loyal, responsible, colorful, sensitive, of rich imagination and early maturity of judgment." But these men and women carry the burdens of "retreats into fantasy, marked insecurities, obsessiveness, sleepwalking, anxieties, snobbishness, intolerance, fears, hostilities, procrastinations." The examiners expect the constructive elements here to overcome the destructive ones, but the chances for success seem greater than the chances for happiness. It is interesting that two of the strongest of these students have already sought help in analysis.

4. In the three groups already described, the examiners felt that the balance was on the constructive side, but about this next

group of nine students they were doubtful. Again there is high intelligence in all, and, in different individuals, ability to work hard, idealism, frankness, and "a rich and gifted personality." But there are alarming liabilities: depressed and schizoid states, obsessions, coldness, sadism, "a precarious bizarre balance," conversion symptoms.

Let me suggest that the student council group is a fair sample of four *different kinds* of normality. All its members are succeeding in their main purpose in their special situation—succeeding at college. Some are young people, gifted, easy, and happy; some are steady and modest; some have many gifts and many neurotic traits and seem bound for success rather than for happiness; and, tentatively, some "normal" students are waging a desperate war with destructive forces within them but manage to stay on top in a precarious balance.

And now for an indirect approach to the most elusive of all questions—what is normal?

In Chapters IV–VII different groups of individuals were arranged in lines according to the amount of normality there was in them. This makes it easier to imagine what I suggested in Chapter I—a great line of all the men and women of the United States arranged according to the same criterion. A study of these five lines brings out some facts about human beings which often escape attention and which many of us would prefer to leave in obscurity.

It has already become evident, I think, that not many people will be found to be very near the top or the bottom, either fully normal or fully abnormal. And the groups at both ends of the line will not be too interesting; at least, nothing can be done about them. More interesting, more complicated, more in need of help, are the great majority of us who are 90 per cent to 10 per cent normal and who include the overconscientious, the anxious, the prejudiced, the gifted people, and the rank and file, as well as patients with mild mental diseases. These are the people who elect the President and the Congress and lead in all aspects of our culture. They are our neighbors and our relatives; they are ourselves.

It is also evident that there is no point on the line at which one can say with whole truth, "Those to the right are sane; those to the left, insane. Those to the right are reasonable; those to the left, without reason." To be sure, all those in the top 10 per cent are sane, sometimes uncomfortably so. All those in the last 10 per cent are insane, sometimes in complete comfort. But everywhere else in the line it can only be said that an individual is a little saner than someone on one side of him and a little less sane than someone on the other. A man can look to right or left, and as far as he can see he will find people like himself; there will be his own prejudice and, to his surprise, his own special fear. (A woman who had a fear of riding on a commuter's train told me that on a trip from my office to her home, as she sat trying to conceal her inner agitation, she was bothered by the continuous chatter of a woman who shared her seat. As this woman reached her station she apologized, saying that she talked to relieve her fear of riding on the train.) And where one man's vision ends, another's begins, and the chains of likenesses run all the way.

Thus aggression, recognized and well managed in the husband who let his wife manage the children, shows itself more dangerously when an alcoholic husband beats his wife, and comes to a climax when a schizophrenic soldier kills a prisoner.

This lack of sharp definitions should help legislators and voters to think of the patients in large state hospitals as people like themselves. In reality, these likenesses are so great as to be frightening.

The line of the normal, more or less, reminds everyone that "nothing human is alien to myself." As Mark Twain said, "I become more convinced that I and other men are alike, and that what virtues I have are the virtues of others, while the vices of others are all to be found in me." * And Voltaire put it in a

---

* As quoted in Gamaliel Bradford's *Life and I*. Houghton Mifflin, Boston, 1928.

beautiful sentence: "With a little imagination and one's own heart, one may understand everything in humanity." * The more the normal and abnormal activities of men and women are studied the more they tend to coalesce.

It is surprising that there are no satisfactory definitions for such important things as mind and sanity, health and normality. This means that there is no exact definition of neurosis, illness, or delusion. Yet all these terms must be used without apology— they are useful. More or less, an individual is sane, neurotic, healthy, or delusional.

Hazy definitions, or rather descriptions, are often important *because they are true.* The thing or the person described *is* often hazy. You cannot exactly describe or define love or loyalty or many other important qualities. I have always disliked hearing a physician try to pin a patient down to an exact statement when the patient is trying to describe a vague mood or idea. How can you describe a haze in exact and clear-cut terms? If you could, it would be a haze no longer.

Standing back for another look, we see that we can learn different things from the three great, natural sections of the line.

People toward the top teach the values of balance, integrity, steadiness, ease, and happiness.

The people in the center cannot be summed up so simply and acceptably. Here we meet power and weakness, sometimes in the same person, along with conflict, brilliance, creativeness, variability, despair, and ecstasy. From previous chapters I recall men who suffered in depressions and then became "the spark plug of our business," "the man everyone follows," "the man who has more original and sound ideas than all of us put together," the teacher who "thinks only of his pupils and inspires them." I recall Abraham Lincoln, writers and artists, Joshua Logan, Alfred Lord Tennyson.

People of the mid-section call attention to the drawbacks that accompany talent and genius. "Una was the least gifted and best balanced one in the family," is a shrewd sentence from a

* As quoted in Gamaliel Bradford's *Life and I.* Houghton Mifflin, Boston, 1928.

novel. Intelligence, talent, and genius predispose to trouble as well as to success and recognition. Trouble comes from such a matter-of-fact thing as keeping a boy with a talent for the violin or piano from playing baseball because he might stiffen a finger, and it comes from such an intangible thing as asking searching questions about men and nature—an easy highway to trouble in our society.

To be gifted means to be different from the crowd. Again I claim that while fundamental likenesses are to be found from one end of the line to the other, there would be no line at all if there were not the precious differences that make each unit of the line an individual. Vive la différence! There is not much point in education unless it makes people different, and exactly here is where education in the United States is rapidly losing ground—to Russia, of all nations. In Russia, all standards in upper schools and colleges and universities are high, though narrow, and as soon as a student reaches his limit he is dropped—to find work at his proper level. While one student is like every other in his responses to fundamental pressures, there is no fundamental law that says that all students are equal in musical or engineering ability, in athletics or intelligence. In the United States it is agreed that education should cultivate "the little excellences of the many," but it should also cultivate the great excellencies of the few. As matters now stand, a degree from a Russian university has a definite meaning, while a degree from a college or university in this country means very little. If everyone has a college degree, then no one has a college degree that is worth much.

In our world, which sets so much store on uniformity and conformity, the gifted person meets more than his share of unreasoning opposition and is made miserable by those who want him to fall in line and toe the mark of mediocrity. Does this make him more neurotic? When he was a child he was thrown among children who mercilessly demanded that he conform, and he was placed in schools geared to the average run of pupils.

This is why a wise educator has said, "Many truants are good boys running away from a bad school."

Sometimes I have been called upon to speak to postgraduate students trained for medicine or the arts or sciences, whose long training had accentuated their gifts and made them more difficult to live with. They had become "expert, proficient, and lopsided." So I have told them, not altogether in jest, that it might be better for them, immediately upon graduation, to retire to a sanitarium and stay there. Sometimes a laboratory or a library would do as well. There they would find stable conditions of life, tempered winds, helping hands to keep them steady. They would not be distressed by their differences from the crowd, because they would not see the crowd and would not be under any compulsion to accept or imitate the crowd's ways and customs. Bases for invidious comparisons would be absent. For a certain price, probably a high price, they would find unending tolerance and sympathy, which, by the way, are standard equipment of a good mental hospital. The world of common sense would be kept outside the walls, together with the butcher and baker and candlestick maker who insist upon treating all people alike. They might consider "the world well lost" in exchange for peace of mind and comfort of body. And if one of them wanted to spend twenty years in writing a book, as a friend of mine did, with no expectation that anyone would ever read it, he would have that privilege. Similarly, many artists in the Middle Ages sought sanctuary and protection in the monasteries, with satisfaction all around.

To connect "gifted" people with neuroses, as I have done, may make it easier for a reader to accept the idea that there could be some neurosis in him. But there are some people who turn this notion inside out, saying, "I am so unbalanced, so unconventional, that I must be a genius." This book may confirm their suspicions or it may persuade them to find some better excuse or explanation for their behavior.

To be a real genius isn't much fun, as all history tells us.

Geniuses tend to have prejudices against the common herd, and the herd is likely to have prejudices against them. This may lead the genius to the conviction that the herd, the well-ordered life, and the conventions of society are all inventions of the devil. It has been said that genius is a "divine release from inhibitions," but, if so, it must be very hard on the neighbors. They may not be willing to allow the genius to share certain privileges with mental patients or with children—to be peculiar in dress, to be open and even insulting in speech, to be unashamed of having emotions, to be impractical and shiftless.

And now, after a short look at the ease and happiness of the top of the line and a long look at the turmoil and brilliance of the center, I turn to some of the wonderful teachers who make up the low end of the line.

Chapter IX

NORMAL IS
A PASSING MARK

MENTAL PATIENTS have much to say to all of us who at the moment are more normal. Over twenty-five years ago I began to understand this truth:

Mental patients are fighting our battles for us and much of their fighting is out in the open. A knight in the tournament wears an identifying shield and color; he is all Sorrowful, or all a Daydreamer, or all Activity or all Suspicion. There is no doubt about him, no half-way measures.

But in the everyday struggles which we all go through there is no such plain marking. A knight fights under a dozen different colors, and tries to deceive us about what caused his success or defeat. A cloud of dust envelops the field and we may wonder what the fight was about, or whether it was worth the trouble. But the mental patient wears his heart on his sleeve, as the knight of chivalry wore his lady's glove or garter. He stays under the same color, come what may; he carries his one quality or characteristic to its logical conclusion. His unwillingness to compromise may lead him to disaster, but it allows the bystander to know what happens when alleviated unselfishness, unmitigated reasoning or disordered or confused states of mind and emotions are carried to extremes.

And we may be comforted to find that amid the turmoil of modern life there still remain some allegories to guide us.*

We need the obvious exaggerations that can be seen in the moods, twisted ideas, and even the hallucinations of severe

* E. D. Bond, "To a Graduating Class of Geniuses," *Mental Hygiene*, Vol. 13, pp. 520-28, (July) 1929.

psychoses. And we need the flashes of deep insight they give us from time to time. In a moment of desperation mental patients throw off the covers which most people wrap about their deeper secrets. A young man exclaims, "I want to cut my mother up into little pieces and devour her." A prim school principal says, "I'll have a child by myself or by my father." It needs no analysis to discover here infantile sexuality carried into adult life; it cries out for recognition.

If a reader keeps the line of the normal, more or less, in mind and can remember some of the comments made by people under stress about themselves, about congressmen, parents, relatives, people in general, he will be ready to take in stride and to make use of the amazingly frequent references in newspapers and magazines to psychiatric matters.

Take a look at one page of the New York *Times* Book Review section of February 26, 1956. On it appear these phrases—"a divided temperament," "morbid and neurotic," "an attack of hysterical blindness," "a wry and melancholy imagination," "personal obsessions of disaster"—all referring to the author William March. In this author's stories one heroine "goes mad and returns to her dolls"; another "burns her vicious husband," for there are no Greek Furies to avenge the unacknowledged crimes against humanity. In a review of another book on the same page, we are told that the hero "lost his memory" and "lost in the private night of his brain" was driven to distraction by the shock of happening upon "his father and mother in the act of love."

And then turn to the New York *Herald Tribune* of March 2, 1956. John Crosby, radio and television columnist, writes of a horse named Psychotherapy running in the third race at Hialeah and says, "Psychiatric terminology has invaded every other field. Let's keep it out of horse racing. . . . Well, what was the parentage of Psychotherapy? Out of Mother Hate by Father Image, I expect. Probably [he will] sire a lot of colts named Neurotic, Sibling Rivalry and Oedipus Conflict. Next thing you know, they'll be naming Pullman cars Hysterical Blindness. This thing has got to stop."

Perhaps Mr. Crosby need not worry too long. There is now in the racing circuit a stallion named Bureaucracy. Here is a horse that should push Psychotherapy into oblivion.

I know that the lines show that I have made arbitrary judgments in putting one person above another with reference to a normality which has not yet been defined. To justify my opinions and to continue a search for the elusive normal, I shall try to describe my way of looking at people, and especially my way of placing those who come to me for help.

As I face a new, unknown person with an unknown problem I want to make or be furnished with the results of medical or neurological examinations. Without these data a psychiatric diagnosis is founded on sand; I don't want to call a person neurotic who has a brain tumor or an acute toxic condition.

I begin by supposing that the person is normal, give or take a few symptoms. A man consulted me about taking an important position in another state. "What will the change do to my family?" he asked. "I want to talk this over with someone not personally interested in whether I go or stay." The only contribution I made was to advise this man to announce his decision not to appoint a relative to any position when he took his new job. On leaving he said, "Putting my cards on the table before a disinterested person has helped me to make up my mind to go." But I had not told him to go—or not to go.

Some years ago a wife was admitted as a voluntary patient at the Pennsylvania Hospital. It was soon seen that she was a well person and that her husband, a doctor, was abnormally suspicious. The wife begged permission to remain in the hospital until her husband could be persuaded to become a patient himself. This was a curious case and an enlightening one.

In a baseball park there were two unusual people. One was James Pearsall, a man recovered from a severe mental disease, playing his position with concentration and skill. Another was a man who for eighteen innings, monotonously and without sense, reason, or understanding—to say nothing of human sympathy—kept yelling "crazy, crazy, crazy!" For once we have a clear-cut situation—on that day Pearsall was normal and the man who yelled was abnormal.

But what is a "mental case," anyway? A conference of the Millbank Foundation once discussed this question and ran into the inevitable quandaries. Is a "case" a person who must turn to a psychiatrist for help? The most difficult cases do not turn for help. For the teacher, is a "case" a child whose behavior is not like that of other children? William Henry Chamberlain, the successful writer, was a "lone wolf" in school and college; Winston Churchill's behavior in school was astonishingly different from the behavior of his fellows. Is a "case" a person with a disordered relationship to the people about him? Sometimes a person gets along very well socially, but is unhappy inside himself.

A good example of the difficulty in making maladjustment the sign of a "case" is given as follows. "I feel too hot at this conference. I take off my tie and then my coat. I am still adjusted. I take off my pants—I am maladjusted." How about a person rebelling against Hitler's society, or Stalin's, or some aspects of our own? Are they, too, to be considered and called "cases"? A "case," we may say, is a person who fails to reach his "normal goals" or who has "abnormal" ones. But what are normal goals?

Normality is a passing mark, and it is a direction, a goal. This is as true of bodies as it is of minds. Many men and women physically have a passing mark in that they are able to do their work even if they have poor posture, decayed and repaired teeth, vision which needs glasses. It is difficult to define exactly a normal heart; some champion distance runners have had what in a sick person would be described as valvular heart disease. Men and women, mentally and physically, reach for the normal, approach the normal, go toward a goal.

I have always been careful to look for normal explanations of abnormal behavior. An essentially normal person will become irritable because of great outside stresses and recover as those stresses are removed. But a neurotic person may break on receiving a promotion. What is normal or abnormal thinking and acting under brain-washing? The thinking of the brain-washed prisoner may be normal under the circumstances.

I am in accord with a sentence I found in a magazine: "A thorough psychiatric examination will discover a streak of normality in almost everyone." The wide streak at the top of the line narrows as it goes down, but it is always there.

I believe that psychiatrists, instead of thinking that everybody is queer, are inclined to see normality where no one else sees it. They may overdo this tendency, but to them normality is not a narrow path, not a chalk line, but a very wide road with somewhat hazy margins. To psychiatrists, people are more normal than otherwise.

But let us return to the method of approach to the problem presented by a new patient. After a certain amount of attention to evidences of normality, I probably shall have noticed and been told that the person before me has a special problem. It could be alcoholism, and if so, he or she needs a special treatment.

The next step is to consider a possible neurosis and a tangle of loves and hates of infinite variety. What I want to know first is easy enough. Does this person have anxiety inappropriate to the occasion, the time, and the place? Is he trying to ward this off by rituals, by physical symptoms, or by other evasive maneuvers?

And at the end of a first interview I look for sweeping moods of depression or exhilaration which show up in the words and actions of the patient. I look for delusions and hallucinations, and I notice especially any signs that a man or woman is retiring from a real world into a place of his or her own.

From the beginning of the examination, I have had in mind that a part of the brain may be damaged and that in older peo-

ple severing of nerve paths may bring about such mental symptoms of physical illness as confusion and lack of memory.

All this is an outline, a preliminary view which postpones
considering complications until later.

But all the time I have other questions to ask of all the people in this outline, whether they are normal, alcoholic, neurotic,
or psychotic. The four questions are as important for one group
as another, for a successful businessman—or a patient in a state
hospital.

What has he got? What are his assets in intelligence, in
musical ability, in mechanical skill? In respect to these, the
question can have a rather exact answer. But what does he have
in steadiness, loyalty, and perseverance—attributes more difficult
to measure?

What does he want? What are his objectives in religion, in
marriage, in work, in his social life? A man's dominant purpose
or ruling love can reveal the whole man.

What does he think of himself? Here we encounter difficulties,
for many men try to conceal their estimates of themselves. But
there are helpful signs and symptoms. If he is boastful, if he
shows off and is intolerant, it may indicate that he doesn't
think he is worth much. If he is insecure, he may try to hide it
by bluffing and bullying others. On the other hand, too much
self-esteem may be hinted by excessive demands on others, on
parents, friends, and even the universe. A proper self-respect—
which is a wonderful thing—is shown by willingness and ability
to accept advice, help, and criticism. The self-respecting man is
also able to give and take orders, to defend his own rights and
the rights of others.

What are his habitual ways of dealing with difficulties such
as opposition, failure, or the responsibilities of success? Meeting an obstacle along the way, does he usually make a frontal
attack upon it or does he prefer to find a way around it? Or does
he sit down to think about it? He may even run away or wait
for reinforcements before he tackles it. This question, we shall

see later, leads to the discussion of the habits, mental mechanisms, or dynamisms which pull people up or down.

This explanation of how I think in a first interview may help a reader to see why I put one individual ahead of another in the line. While I wish that every reader would make his own line, I feel sure that the reader's general reasoning would have to be somewhat like my own and that certain ideas about the normal would be the same on all arrangements.

The very act of arranging the lines often helps in understanding the elusive normal. At once it is evident that *normal means a passing mark, not perfection.* At the bottom of the scale, mental patients show that a small segment, perhaps 10 per cent, of their minds may function normally while all the rest is in utter disorder. This small segment of rationality, as we go up the scale, gradually becomes larger until about 90 per cent is reached. But then, in the few people remaining, there is at least a sliver of the abnormal in a prejudice, overconscientiousness, or inappropriate anxiety. Over and over I have to repeat that in default of any sharp dividing line a person must be normal *enough* to vote, to sign a deed or will—normal *enough* to make valid whatever he intends to do.

In spite of this evident truth, there is still a general tendency to think in terms of all or nothing.* "I am 100 per cent normal or I am crazy!" People approach panic when they see some unreason in themselves. But if people could get a better idea of how reason and unreason, controlled thinking and blind emotion, civilized and savage notions are intertwined in everyone, they could live more confidently and seek help more easily. Perhaps that is a contribution a book like this can make.

And in forming the line, normal has never been equated with average. Benjamin Franklin, far above most men in gifts, is the personification of the normal. A woman with an intelligence

* The remainder of the chapter is taken, with some changes in order, from an article entitled "The Student Council Study, An Approach to the Normal," which I wrote for the *American Journal of Psychiatry* and which was published in their July, 1952, issue (Vol. 109, pp. 11–16).

far above average may be normal. The conceptions of normal and average are separate.

Neither does normal mean uninteresting. In a current play there is a wife who is disturbed because her husband is "faithful and normal"; in a current novel an author says that rationality is a token of a drab soul. I can sympathize, in moderation, with the effort to take interest and to find beauty in the deviate and the criminal; I cannot abide the refusal to see beauty and interest in steady, kindly, hard-working, law-abiding citizens. They are sometimes condemned because they are conventional, which means that they have adopted customs that have been proved agreeable to other people. I repeat that many who are prejudiced against the normal are thinking, "I am a misfit, and so I must be interesting—perhaps a genius." But the shallowness of a person who thinks himself or herself interesting *because* he or she is a misfit arouses little attention in the psychiatrist, and no enthusiasm. "Look at me because I am unfaithful, alcoholic, unstable!" The patient who says so is usually following a too-familiar pattern, demanding attention with exaggerated or imaginary problems.

A normal person has problems enough to make him interesting to anyone who looks under the surface. Anna Freud discusses the production of anxiety as a normal function of the mind and not a neurotic manifestation. General Omar Bradley writes, "Where there are people there is pride and ambition, prejudice, and conflict. In Generals as in other men, capabilities cannot always hide weakness nor can talents hide faults."

After these negative ideas about the normal, I think I ought to put forward some positive descriptions. It is not easy to do so, for there are on record few psychiatric studies of happy and successful people. This is unfortunate, as has been pointed out by Brewster Smith. He says, "Until normal people, happy and engrossed in their human relationships and work, have been studied with some of the perspicacity and thoroughness that have been expended on the troubled and deviant, speculation about mental health must remain highly tentative."

Many attempts have been made to paint the picture of a normal person. I have read hundreds of definitions and descriptions, and I do not know how much of the three sentences that follow is my own and how much is a summary of many opinions. But the sentences, I think, are useful and constructive.

1. Normality has a wide range and is in a state of flux.

2. Normal people are free to focus their energies, their gifts large or small, on main purposes.

3. In their own culture, normal people work and love with ease, happiness, and efficiency somewhat in proportion to their circumstances.

A description of people in mental health is given in a widely publicized statement of the National Association for Mental Health. "They feel comfortable about themselves [one hopes, not too comfortable]; they feel right about other people—they can like and trust others; they are able to meet the demands of life."

In one sense (Adlerian), the normal person is a harmless one; any destructive tendencies are under control. In another sense (Ernest Jones), the normal person is fearless, free of inappropriate anxiety.

However, there is another way of describing normality and that is to consider it as maturity, which in its different aspects offers some opportunities for measurement.

Chapter X

ACTING ONE'S AGE

AN IMPORTANT CONSIDERATION keeps the idea of mental normality from being too indefinite or too difficult to measure. It is obvious that normality changes with every state of life and will be shown differently at ages of 5, 15, 21, or 30. We may say, therefore, that a person who feels, thinks, and acts as he should at his age, whatever it may be, is more or less normal, while the one who behaves at fifty like a child of ten is certainly not.

The yardstick is the concept of emotional maturity, of "acting one's age," of being fully grown up. To a considerable extent, the different aspects of this maturity can be crudely measured. It is helpful to use this yardstick, even though it is not completely accurate, in trying to put people close to their proper places along the line which starts from normal and goes downward.

Along this line there are no children, but there is much childishness. Not so much at the top, where people generally "act their ages," but toward the middle of the line there are people somewhat adolescent, too much interested in themselves, insecure, and changeable. At the bottom of the line, near its very end, are some who have regressed to childhood, some who live in a childish make-believe world, some who need protection as a child does.

The main purposes of life, to which normal people should devote their attention and energies, change with every year of life. What is demanded of a person of twenty-one is almost the opposite of what is expected of a baby. And so, normality is the ability to grow.

It is useful to consider the terms in which we would describe a normal, healthy baby at the age of four months. The baby should be dependent, selfish, irresponsible, and uncontrolled. He has no conception of time or of right and wrong. The baby is "integrated," as psychiatrists say, because he is all in one piece. He wants what he wants when he wants it, which is as it should be, because he has had no chance to build up controls over his emotions or appetites. A human baby has a long road to go and a great deal to learn, while a baby guinea pig only a few hours old can walk, run, and swim. But, as the late Dr. Macfie Campbell remarked, "After all, the personality of a guinea pig is rather limited."

But to return to the human baby. As an infant he begins a reasonably consistent and well-planned intellectual education for life. He is given a well-thought-out ladder on which to climb. Its steps are the nursery school, the kindergarten, the first to sixth grades, the junior and senior high school, and perhaps the college and postgraduate course. His intellectual growth from childhood to adulthood is mainly in the hands of professionals, the teachers who may or may not know their business but are supposed to know it. Educators are constantly trying to improve and lengthen the ladder, until, for many Americans, it extends ten years or more beyond the age at which their great-grandfathers were considered sufficiently educated for all practical purposes. It is not yet a perfect ladder, but it is pretty good.

But the infant also began another education soon after he first fell out of his cradle—a training for loving and living with other people. This is emotional training, essential to the child's progress toward maturity. But where do we find order and arrangement in it? Where is the grading? Where is the curriculum? Instead, we are likely to see such a haphazard, hit-or-miss guidance of the growing child's emotions that it is amazing that any survive it to become well-balanced and healthy-minded adults.

In comparison, intellectual schooling shows a remarkable consistency and progression. When a boy has learned the multiplication table he can rely upon it later; nobody tries to pull it out from under him. Using it for a foothold, he can move on to more advanced mathematics. In geometry no one tries to replace an early theorem by the one proposed by an interesting school-boy: "Things equal to the same thing are equal to anything else."

But much of a child's early emotional experience has no stability at all. Attacks upon and substitutions for early theorems are attempted constantly. The first lesson in the book says that "Mother love is everything good." But then the mother refuses to feed the child when he thinks he is hungry or makes him wash his face when he would sooner be dirty. Worse yet, she tries to keep him a baby. Now another lesson says that "Mother love is cruel, the origin of all evil." To the adolescent, mother love can be something else, a nagging criticism and interference with a child's personal and private growth.

Emotional attitudes may be fixed in us for life unless we unlearn them. What we learn from an unhappy experience should be discarded when it turns out to be mistaken and untrue. How much more trustworthy is the multiplication table, which always "stays put."

The psychiatrist knows that twisted attitudes do survive in some adults who should have outgrown and discarded them. John, for example, was a helpless baby when a woman allowed his feet to freeze. He has not forgotten it, though it happened long ago and he cannot consciously remember it. Now he wants nothing more to do with women, and the psychiatrist is trying to persuade him to unlearn the lesson of long ago and discover that women can be agreeable creatures to have around.

Fortunately, matters are not so hopeless as they may seem. Something within the healthy child offsets many of the mistakes and honest blunders of those who train his emotions badly. At the age of four, and even sooner, the child has a wonderful capacity to learn. From the age of six to twelve he grows into acceptance of other children and learns to conform to other people's standards. Usually he bears no resentment against those who said or did the wrong thing when he was younger. Like Topsy, he "just grows" into adolescence. In adolescence he wants to set up his own standards and, inconsistently, to conform to the manners, customs, and styles of his peers. He experiments, questions the competence of his parents, and is likely to become a hero-worshiper, for better or worse. Athletes, movie stars, FBI agents, or gangsters may become his models, though fortunately the adolescent switches loyalties so frequently and easily that no great harm is done by hero-worship. And then, at twenty-one—to accept the conventional turning point—comes the great step of being considered a citizen and, in contrast to the baby, becoming independent, unselfish, responsible, controlled by practical considerations and by conscience.

Teaching of emotional growth is left largely to amateurs, such as the child's parents, some of whom have not mastered their own emotional difficulties and may never do so. But the amateur does have one great advantage over the professional teacher: Parents love their children, or ought to love them, and while love does not "conquer all," it helps.

Emotional growth is frequently influenced by accidental happenings. The death of a parent may wrench the child loose from an anchorage on which he has relied all his short lifetime and may deeply affect his further development. The discovery of a parent's unworthiness can be a similar shock later on. Even a frightening thunderstorm may have far-reaching consequences. A child's misinterpretations of instruction and discipline, of natural phenomena and human behavior, are likely to influence him emotionally rather than intellectually.

In general, we may say that intellectual progress toward maturity can far outrun emotional growth.

What may happen is illustrated by an actual case from the psychiatrist's files: A. and B. were rival professors of physics. When one could muss the paper on the other's desk or upset the other's wastebasket, he gained much satisfaction. Professor A. scored a point when he hid one of Professor B.'s rubbers. The maid who cleaned their offices described them as "two four-year-olds scrapping in a sandpile."

I should apologize for listing the obvious steps in growth toward maturity if I had not seen how many parents were surprised and hurt when their children left one stage for another. Much family unhappiness would be avoided if the parents simply accepted the fact that a child must grow up, must change. If the youngster does *not* change, then his fond parents really have something to worry about.

Patients and their friends have pointed comments to make on different aspects of immaturity. These comments or confessions illustrate failures to achieve independence, unselfishness, heterosexuality, realism, responsibility, a time sense, a sound conscience, steadiness in mood and in purpose, a feeling of security, and integration.

Taking them in this order, we come first to cases in which a patient failed to grow up and act his or her age because of a childish dependence on someone else.

A married woman said to me, "I am tormented when I am with my mother, and I am lost without her."

Another married woman said, "I can't get along without father and mother."

A physician of thirty-one made this remark: "I can't seem to get started in medical practice. There is always something more to learn, another graduate course to take. I have an M.D., M.A., and Ph.D. My father still supports me."

A grown woman told me, "I've got to become independent of mother, but I get more like her every day. Last evening I told her I hated her and sneered at her, and next thing I was weeping on her shoulder."

Here we may recall the case of John Ruskin, the artist-philosopher. At the age of fifty-two he was ruled by his mother, who had previously accompanied him to college and chosen a wife for him. And I have met a college graduate who could not eat a meal unless it had been cooked by his mother!

It is also difficult for many people to outgrow the natural selfishness of childhood. Some cynics say that it can't be done. "Everyone sets his own good before his neighbor's," wrote the Roman poet Terence. But ample experience tells us that this is not true; if it were, the human race might have destroyed itself long since.

Here are a few comments from patients and their friends and relatives which reveal that some unhappy people do carry into adult years the natural selfishness of childhood.

"I am callously, unthinkingly selfish."

"I am too sensitive to see the slums, to clean away the dirt, or to work with unsympathetic people."

"My husband was his mother's favorite and was denied nothing; she paid little attention to the other children. But when she lay dying of cancer, my husband would not go near her. 'To think that my mother would fail me!' he said. 'She can do nothing for me; why should I see her?' "

"Things are vital to John only if they are closely related to himself."

"I try to sympathize with other people, but I end by pitying myself. When I try to look at others, myself gets in the way. It is boring, but I can't help it."

Third in our list of adult childishness is the failure to achieve a satisfactory heterosexual life. Homosexuality plays a larger part in modern living than many people are willing to believe, and it is a familiar phenomenon to the psychiatrist. Patients often talk about it, usually betraying nothing more serious than that they have failed to grow up, though this may be serious enough in some cases. Perhaps the simplest statement is that of a woman, old enough to know better, who told me bluntly that "sex is nothing but a dirty trick of boys!"

Here are a few variations on the same unhappy theme.

"I didn't marry until I was head of a girl's school and completely devoted to girls. At the marriage ceremony I never once looked at my husband, but only at a girl I knew. I tore off my wedding ring and cursed my husband. Then I got chronic colitis. You know, I hated my father and was so glad when mother divorced him."

A similar case is that of a boy who rebelled against his father when he was thirteen. To "get his father's goat" he took on a woman's role; he bought cosmetics, adopted a high-pitched voice, wore his hair long, bought woman's underthings, looked up operations which might change his sex. "This has brought immense relief from the oppression and restriction I used to feel under my father."

"I get dressed up and look at myself in the mirror—that is sex enough for me," declared a young woman.

A man of thirty dreamed: "I was swimming with a lot of naked women. They turned out to be my mother. I ran."

The next category of childishness in grown people is that of running away from reality, and one example will serve. Some readers may smile at the story, but it isn't really funny. A young man got married and then found it impossible to untie himself from his mother's apron strings. After the wedding the groom and his mother departed on a trip to Niagara Falls, leaving a puzzled bride to get the home ready for their return.

Unwillingness to accept responsibility or admit its importance is closely related to this escape from realities.

"I want to be a Queen." When a former motion-picture star said this, it was evident that she thought only of the privileges of royalty and not once of its heavy responsibilities.

Some are actually terrified by responsibility, as this example shows. His mother reported that "Thomas always cried at every promotion in school, when he went into long pants, when he graduated, when a friend married." And, from my friend Dr. Frederick Allen, I have this comment of a ten-year-old boy: "I'd rather be a baby; you get more service."

Unwillingness to keep up with the times may not seem to the reader a symptom of adult childishness. But basically it is a re-treat from reality and an unwillingness to accept the fact of change. Human beings live in a world bounded by space and time, and they should go along with changes, not cling to the past like a child clutching an old doll or a ragged blanket. This failure to achieve a sense of time has been the theme of countless novels and plays, usually involving bitter conflicts between foes of the same household.

Another aspect of changing with the times is the transfer of primary interests from the old family to the new, from parents to wife and children or to adults of our own ages. This implies —and it cannot be said too often—no change in affection, but a change in the direction of that affection. Once a new family is established, the husband and wife have a first loyalty to each other and then to their children. The mother-in-law who was first in our first line recognized this; she did not demand her son's affection, and so she received his as well as that of her daughter-in-law. Curiously, the more love a person has for a parent, the easier it is to love a husband or wife or child. But a mingling of hate and love brings disaster. Notice how this married woman of thirty does not seem to live in the present at all. She never talks about her husband or people her own age; she lives in the past.

"Mother poisons me with her disapproval. Mother and father liked my little sister and didn't like me. I need freedom from any family ties. Oh, I hate my mother—what shall I do? I don't want to look at mother or father. A terrible hatred eats away at me. Mother is trying to turn me against my faith—I've declared war on her."

Waging a childhood war at the age of thirty!

"My father and mother look backward to my grandfather's time," I was told by their troubled daughter. "They are two generations behind, and they don't see that we should be educated for the future and not the past. They might as well accept the fact that time goes by; it goes whether they accept it or not."

Here is another case involving conflict between the past and present. "We lived in a two-hundred-year-old house with my grandparents and great-aunts and father and mother. Everybody talked about how old things were best. Father knows everything there ever was to know about everything that is useless. He won't work; he argues instead. Mother was a model child; now she is a lady who thinks she is unselfish, but she never had any pleasure in us children and educated us for the last century. My sister rebelled and goes her own way; she ridicules us. I am the model child, and I'm always sick. It's the only way I can live behind the times."

It is equally childish to live always in the future, like the Dickens character who was always dead broke and always confident that "something will turn up." Daydreams run wild, like those of a child, in those who dismiss the dreary present to build fairy castles in tomorrow's sky. The following are the statements of exhilarated persons (the opposite of the depressives), who forget the lessons of the past and their present limitations. Compare them, if you please, to the boastful imagination of a small boy, or even to the rash promises of a young lover, if not to the promises of advertising.

"Stay with me and you'll wear diamonds. I'm going on the radio with a new idea. Yesterday it cost me $47.50 to talk to Hollywood. I've new ideas, millions of 'em; Wall Street will be an easy mark." This patient jumps rapidly from one subject to another, but radio, Hollywood, and Wall Street being what they are, some of his ideas may eventually make him wealthy.

And a real estate promoter promises, "The city hall will be here and the public library there. Here are broad avenues; here a house with a beautiful view. No, you can't go to see these things yet, but look at these blueprints." This man could be quite sane, of course, and as normal as his business or profession permits him to be. But many who talk like him are in mental hospitals.

The importance of achieving a sound conscience will be considered in Chapter XII. The failure to do so is evidence of adult childishness. Usually it takes the form of adherence to childhood codes which common sense has failed to replace with adult standards. For example, parents stress perfection too much, and later their son or daughter complains that "I can't compromise," or declares that "I mustn't make friends because they might lower my standards." Another tells me that he "can't bear to see anyone sitting down doing nothing."

Here is a typical perfectionist talking to the psychiatrist. "I am compelled to work hard six days a week. I hate Sundays, when the library closes and shuts me out. I was taught to be perfect in everything I did. Now I begrudge anything that keeps me away from work, and my work grows more and more inefficient."

Another patient who was very tired and very tense was given an extra two-week vacation. A friend let him use his sailboat. "If I went out by myself or with my wife I was constantly distressed by the thought that I should have taken the neighbors, who had no boat. If, on the other hand, I did take out those neighbors I was constantly worried by the necessity to entertain them and be responsible for their safety. I was as tired on the last day as I was on the first." So he returned to his work exhausted, tense, and ineffective.

"Conscience does make cowards of us all," said Hamlet, who was an excellent example of the self-conscious neurotic. But more often a misguided conscience of childhood makes it difficult for us to think, feel, or act like adults.

To get a look at the most valued aspect of the grown-up personality, let us glance at a few quotations from the New York Times of July 20, 1952.

The noble habit of doing nothing at all is being neglected in a degree which seems to me to threaten the degeneration of the whole race.—G. K. Chesterton.

Time you enjoy wasting is not wasted time.—Anon.

If you can spend a perfectly useless afternoon in a perfectly useless manner, you have learned how to live.—Lin Yu Tang.

These, I think, are grown-up people talking. Grown-up consciences are affirmative, assign proper time for work and rest and play, compromise in matters which have no ethical connection, drive ahead and get the important things done, love more. "Humility means that we do not bother ourselves too much about our own imperfections. Let us be what we are and strive to be that well," said a Saint of old.

Steadiness in mood and purpose is an adult characteristic. It is rarely found in young children and might be considered a disturbing symptom if it were. Longfellow was right when he said that "a boy's will is the wind's will, and the thoughts of youth are long, long thoughts." That is as it should be. But to be grown up means that we have put away childish things and settled down. Those who have failed to do so talk like this.

"I resent almost everybody because I am not sure of myself. . . . I can't sleep away from home. . . . When I was four or five I prayed for a baby brother, and I got a sister, and night and day I think of the injustice of it." The age of the woman who said this was thirty!

"I slap Sally, and I cuddle her," says another. "There is no sense in it, and she doesn't know what to expect, and I don't either."

"I never know how I am going to feel when I wake up in the morning." A small symptom of lack of purpose, but not a trivial one.

Lack of integration speaks for itself in the patient's complaint that "I am all dispersed; I can't manage myself." Or in the common phrases: "He had a breakdown and went to pieces." "He is all broken up." "He is rattled." Obviously, one can't rattle unless one is in at least two pieces!

More serious is the case history of an ultraconventional, conservative lawyer of fifty who said to a friend, his physician, "Soon you will hear that I am going to marry X. I know she is practically a woman of the streets; she will probably ruin me." Within a year of the marriage he killed himself. In him had been an overwhelming, blind force in a place separate from the rest of him, a sad example of lack of integration.

And now, in the same order, come a few comments on success in the growth process—obviously from much happier people.

"Father and mother enjoyed and encouraged every step toward independence we children took."

A girl of twelve said to her mother, who tried to dominate every moment of her life, "From now on I am going to live my own life and not yours." She not only made good this declaratin of independence, but kept on good terms with her mother.

The ability to love, not as a child loves, but as a person in marriage, is a long way from the infant's normal self-centeredness. Here is an admirable example, as reported by a parent: "My daughter in her marriage does not take away her love from us. But she centers her love on her husband and baby, and she looks forward to other children and a new home, not the old one. We have always enjoyed seeing her move gracefully from one stage to another."

A politician who faced facts was Sir Winston Churchill. "I have nothing to offer," he told the British people, "but blood, toil, tears and sweat." Queen Elizabeth II, too, meets squarely the obligations that surround the throne, the endless public appearances, the responsibilities of balancing a private and a public life. This is the antithesis of running away from responsibility like a spoiled child.

"My husband and I are learning things about our child as we go along," says a sensible wife and mother. "We are trying to do nothing for him that he can do himself. That's hard, because we can do it so much better and faster. We are putting something aside for his future education, though it seems a long way off." Here is thought for the morrow, but in practical terms of the present.

Here are fragments of testimony about people who have learned to act their age, in their own words or the words of their friends. They are in strong contrast to the troubled thoughts of those who are bound by a childish conscience, afraid of reality, unable to accept responsibility, unsteady in purpose or mixed-up and unintegrated. They are about people who have grown up, whatever else may be the matter with them.

"I believe in doing the best I can under the circumstances."

"I have a strong religious feeling that makes me happy."

"My husband has a benevolent conscience; he gets things done."

"He is rather dull, but reliable. You know he will always do his best and never let you down."

"He can argue without getting mad."

"He is strong and was a good athlete. He has a nice easy attitude toward other people. He never looks for trouble. He likes changes, new ideas, new people."

"She can take advice, but she makes up her own mind."

"He got hold of himself."

"He pulled himself together and sank the crucial putt."

"My sister is cool and collected."

Examples of success in reaching maturity give a partial picture of the normal. That is, the fully developed man lives his own life, helps others, sees facts, takes responsibility, looks ahead, has a positive, constructive conscience, is steady, accepts advice and changes, and keeps control of himself.

The reader has noted, no doubt, that the suggested aspects of childish behavior in adults are not sharply separated, one from another. For example, the lack of a sense of responsibility implies the lack of a sound conscience, steadiness, and integration. And in maturity, independence involves a willingness to face facts. The different aspects of maturity obviously melt into one another.

Similarly, individuals do not hold a fixed place in the line in respect to their achievement of adulthood. They are constantly shifting their positions, helped or hindered by certain universal upward or downward pulls which will be discussed later.

A rough maturity rating can be made by giving a person ten

points or less for each of these aspects. He may be allowed only
five in respect to responsibility but seven for unselfishness, and
so forth. The ideal and impossible standard of perfection would
be a score of 100. On the other hand, the ultimate tragedy would
be found in the adult with a high intelligence quotient—say
150—and a maturity rating of only 50 or less.

Judged in this way or any other, has the United States as a
whole grown up? The answer is both "yes" and "no," which
shows that the question is unanswerable; it can be answered with
respect to some individuals in our line, which includes all the
adult inhabitants of the United States. But as a people we are
not grown up if we are judged by our advertising, our political
campaigns, and most of our motion pictures. Yet we are adult,
certainly, if measured by our acceptance of election results and
by the best of our plays on the stage, screen, radio, and television.

Nobody has commented on this subject with more discern-
ment than Walter Lippmann in his *A Preface to Morals*.

The successful passage into maturity depends . . . on a breaking-
up and reconstruction of those habits which were appropriate only to
our earliest experience. . . . For unless a man has acquired the
character of an adult, he is a lost soul no matter how good his technical equipment. . . .

The critical phase of human experience . . . is the passage from
childhood to maturity; the critical question is whether childish habits
and expectations are to persist or to be transformed. We grow older.
But it is by no means certain that we shall grow up. The human
character is a complicated thing, and its elements do not necessarily
march in step. It is possible to be . . . [both] shrewd and foolish,
[both] serene and irritable . . . not infrequently we participate in
the enterprises of an adult with the mood and manners of a child.*

This we do when we play and watch games and forget they
are only games—when we grow angry about them and make

* Walter Lippmann, *A Preface to Morals*. The Macmillan Company, New York,
1929, pages 183 and 184.

silly excuses when the wrong team wins. Most of us balk oc-
casionally at the hurdles in the path of adult living and turn to go
back to an easier highway. Many of us daydream when we have
better things to do but don't want to do them. Few of us, if
any, are always wise and steadfast, putting away childish things
forever because we have outgrown them. Perhaps the world
would be a duller place if we were.

But the measure of a man, or one of the measures, is still his
ability and willingness to act his age.

So far we have left untouched the human phenomenon of
growth into goodness. The word "goodness" is used for lack of
a better one; it comprises the elements that may have little to
do with learning or intelligence, but much to do with morality,
kindness, compassion, and a true conscience. We know instinctively that some people are "better" than others; we cannot
always explain or define their goodness.

Someone, I hope, will try to form a line of human beings with
the best on top and the worst at the bottom. Often a person will
have the same place on a scale of the good and on a scale of the
normal. But often an abnormal person will be found to be very
good. I should place the five mildly depressed men mentioned in
Chapter III in the 45 to 49 per cent position as to normality
and the 90 per cent position as to goodness.

And here is a man who for fifteen years has believed that he
was being persecuted; now, with some exaggerated notions of
the importance of his ideas, he is unselfishly devoting most of his
time and effort to improving the well-being of all of us. "My
knowledge of psychiatry is nil, and the facts on which I base
my deductions may not be correct, but I trace some of the emotional insecurity of today to the economic insecurity of the
past." The letters he writes to the President of the United States
show his concern for others and his burning desire to diminish
the fears which now burden civilization. Without success, he
tries to help in ways which he considers constructive but which

society regards as a nuisance. Is he 35 per cent normal and 90 per cent good?

It is impossible to escape the fact that in certain aspects of maturity there is an overlapping of the normal and the good. We ask that a mature person be unselfish, responsible, sound in conscience, and integrated—with its intimations of integrity, honesty, wholeheartedness. These are the basic elements of goodness, as they are of maturity.

In widely read books there is a rejection of these ideas. On the stage and in many modern books there is an underlying assumption that only the weaknesses of people are interesting and that all people are complex creatures who do not understand themselves or their neighbors. Interesting characters are those who are carried downstream by forces they do not understand.

But it is superficial to assume that the normal person, pulling together all his complexities, his abilities, and his imperfections, managing his neuroses, is not an interesting bit of humanity. Think of the complexities of people like Dante, Gandhi, Schweitzer. Authors who focus on the abnormal and pride themselves on being sophisticated are in reality describing an exaggerated, rather obvious and simple way of life; they do not attempt to describe the intricacies of an integrated, normal, *good* human being.

In too many of today's books and plays dis-integrated persons, the bums and tramps and perverts, are regarded as normal and good, as are people who have no goal and literally and figuratively have no place to go. The degraded are exalted. The men and women who strive to meet the demands of maturity, who unselfishly try to provide decent situations for their children, who even go so far as to save something for the future, who have a goal and a place to go—these are uninteresting! If they also want to be clean, they are beneath contempt!

This curious literary flight from maturity inevitably leads the

authors and their characters back to the infantile, to the uncontrolled life which knows only the present.

Can we become fully mature without becoming somewhat
good?

Whitehorn * says that living up to the reasonable expectations
of others in a common enterprise is not an obligation but an
enthusiastic, self-expressive enterprise. Perhaps a psychiatrist
should, as a citizen, help society to lessen its demands for conformity and persuade it, if possible, to make use of the constructive and original forces of many kinds of normal individuals.

Our present social conventions may stifle some people, but
they free many others. To obey the rule to drive on the right
side of the road sets most people free to think of more important
things, even while they are driving. They can save their choices
for more important things.

So it is along the highway of life. The mature person is one
who frees himself from foolish fears, conflicts, and prejudices,
but is willing to surrender some of his lesser freedoms so that
he may choose and act calmly and wisely in more important
matters.

* John C. Whitehorn, professor of psychiatry, Johns Hopkins Medical School;
past-president, American Psychiatric Association.

Chapter XI

CONFLICTS OF PRINCIPLE

THE GROWTH of human beings toward maturity is made a difficult, varied, and interesting affair by apparent conflicts of principles. We tend to set mind against body, freedom against discipline, likeness against difference, the conscious against the unconscious, perfectionism against compromise. Candidates for places in the line of normality are moved up or down by the currents and countercurrents of these opposing principles.

It has been said before that nobody's place in the line is fixed and static. We all have our "ups and downs," our good days and bad. Sometimes we remain tranquil and steady for a considerable period, but at any time our state may change, perhaps suddenly, for better or worse. We may find ourselves "down in the mouth," moody or ill-tempered, worrying too much or working without enthusiasm. At other times we are "sitting on top of the world."

The well-balanced person accepts these fluctuations as normal, which they are. They are something like the alternations of night and day or the cycles of the seasons. They create a healthy climate for our growth, and it is no accident that mankind does its best and most productive work in a temperate but variable physical climate.

But when conflicts of opposing principles within us are responsible for disturbing and distressing changes in our emotions and attitudes, it is time to examine and understand them and see if they can be reconciled.

We shall find that these apparent opposites are not so antag-

onistic as they seem. They may be and should be mutually helpful, not mutually destructive. Former President A. Lawrence
Lowell of Harvard has reminded us that a sailboat can move
against the wind by taking one tack and then another; that we
honor Washington because he carried through a rebellion and
Lincoln because he put one down; that democracies advance by
putting conservatives and progressives alternately into power.

Opposites can be made to interfere with each other or to
help each other. We can have freedom *with* discipline, likenesses *with* differences, the conscious *with* the unconscious.

That "contraries are not mutually exclusive but interde-
pendent" is most easily accepted in the liberal-conservative situation that exists in most democracies. Some think that liberals
make reforms which conservatives hold on to. An extreme liberal
would have a world in continual flux; his opposite, the extreme
conservative, would have it in perpetual stasis. Contradictions
arise if liberals, to bring about changes, turn more and more to
the state, with the result that they create a larger and larger
group of bureaucrats, who are the most conservative people in
the world. And conservatives can carry individualism so far that
liberals rush in to establish the former status quo. But for a
nation to have two parties, and only two, opposing each other
and alternately in power is the way to advance and to hold on to
advances.

An obvious and more or less continuous conflict between
mind and body concerns the psychiatrist and, in less degree, the
doctor. It has been known since ancient times that physical illness can make the mind sick and mental factors can derange
bodily functions. Juvenal gave as the optimum of health "a
sound mind in a sound body." This intimate interplay between
mind and body is an accepted fact.

The doctor, who is seldom a philosopher, does not think of
body as opposing mind. The idea to him is out of order. In any
person brought to him for diagnosis he finds both physical and
mental factors involved, and he decides which is more important

at the time. He knows there are a physical nerve network and a series of glands which are closely tied to the emotions. In these he finds a natural bridge between mind and body—an explanation, for example, of how anxiety makes the heart beat faster. And so he looks ahead to further information about anxiety from those specialists in mental research who use psychoanalysis and psychotherapy. For further explanations about the heart's muscles and nerves he looks to those who specialize in studying its electrical, pharmacological, and pathological changes.

Each set of workers is strongest when it pursues wholeheartedly its own investigations. Both are weakest when they disparage the opposite, but not opposing, group.

Here we have two useful concepts, and we turn first to one and then to the other as we try to help or understand any person. Sometimes our attention turns to a tumor or an infection of the brain, which is damage to the body. Sometimes the psychoanalyst focuses on the relation of a son to his mother, which may be a disorder of the mind. There need be no conflict if we rely first on one principle and then on the other, and if, after investigating the situation on both sides of the bridge, we attack that side which seems to offer a promising opening for treatment.

We are wisely reminded by Henry Maudeley that "man as a whole is a larger affair than any single method of minute inquiry will ever unfold. There is work enough for as many methods for the study of the mind as are rationally based."

We come next to the apparent conflict between freedom and discipline.

For two generations there has been much feeling against domineering parents and much sympathy for children smothered by affection and authority. Many people have gone in for freedom in a big way—the "new freedom" which is neither new nor free. Rousseau, whose own life contradicted nearly everything he wrote, extolled it. Many modern parents, I fear, have tried the "new freedom" on their children and lived to repent it.

The necessity for freedom, which phrase is itself a contradiction in terms, has led many into trouble, as their own words testify.

"At last I am free of father's conservatism and conventionality, and I can lead a revolution." This woman was still dominated by her father, but in reverse. He was driving her from conservatism to its extreme simple opposite, not to the choices of freedom.

Here is exactly the same reaction to authority, but in the other direction: "At last I am free of my parents' liberalism; they are so far to the left. I am going to be a conservative, join the Union League. This country needs to regain the stern ideals of the Founding Fathers."

A typical adolescent joined a familiar chorus when she said, "I want to be free to dress as I please." What she really wanted was to dress in conventional adolescent clothes, to be a slave to style.

Freedom probably means freedom of choice. Pure freedom probably means nothing; it would be like playing football with no rules, no side lines, no goals. It is too loose to be interesting. Everyone has heard of the boy in a "progressive" school who said, "Do I have to do what I want to do today?"

And pure discipline would mean as little. Unfortunately for the world, we have the totalitarian states as examples. But in general there is practical value in discipline, authority, order, convention, boundaries. Otherwise, we would have more statements like this: "Father and mother were pretty uncertain about right and wrong. They couldn't tell us what to do; they set no limits. It was hard on us children."

There is no escape from the recognition that freedom and discipline are parts of the same choice. In the child both should be developed, to be used at the proper time and place. Accelerator and brake in a car do not oppose each other if rightly used; a car moves ahead by use of one strong principle and then the other. To step on the gas and the brake at the same time is like using freedom and discipline at the same time. The resulting conflict is a neurosis.

There is one answer to this apparent conflict. An individual going through life should be able to call wholeheartedly on either freedom or discipline, whichever is needed at the moment.

The great Freud showed a mixture of these principles. From one point of view he was a rebel, a liberator, standing against subjection of a child to a parent; from another he wanted people to be "tractable," and his own son "was well trained not to make superfluous remarks." *

Another conflict, sometimes acute in psychiatric cases, arises between the desire to conform and the desire to be different and individual. These apparent conflicts are so familiar to us in our daily lives that it may be difficult to see why they enter the province of psychiatry at all. The apparent conflict appears in this book, which has as a main theme the idea that people are alike. But in trying to prove it I have put people into a line from one extreme to another, and this in itself is a statement of differences. The differences, as we have seen, extend so far in either direction, toward the top and bottom, that there is a vast gulf between one end of the line and the other. Yet the line is continuous; the differences between one point or person and the next in line is almost imperceptible—though of fundamental importance. I repeat the statement of William James' sagacious carpenter who said: "There is very little difference between one man and another; but what little there is, is very important."

Where lies the conflict, then, and why is the psychiatrist concerned with it? His concern is with the patient who is miserable because he is "different," or thinks he is. He feels that nobody likes him or understands him; he is alone in a crowd, an alien among ordinary people. He broods about it and torments himself with his differences, either nursing them and making them worse or trying desperately to get rid of them, which is also likely to make matters worse.

On the other hand, there are those who wish to be different. They consider themselves hopeless failures because they are drab, ordinary, colorless. They want to be exciting, dramatic,

* Ernest Jones, *Freud: Years of Maturity*. Basic Books, New York, 1955, p. 26.

unusual. They turn to daydreams and delusions to satisfy their discontent with themselves.

The solution, again, lies in the fact that likeness and difference are not incompatible opposites. Again an apparent conflict is not a conflict at all. We need differences in fundamentally similar people. And many a man or woman needs to be persuaded and encouraged to accept his likeness to a host of other people, while making the most of his individual differences. It is differences that make people interesting. The attempt to wipe out differences in totalitarian states is to us a cardinal crime. If fundamentals are alike, variations are all for the best. The best community is not the result of uniformity, but of infinite variety. The strength of a nation lies in both its likenesses and its differences.

In our own country, Republicans and Democrats fight at election time and emphasize their differences, but on closer examination they are both found to be inconsistent, muddleheaded, anxious to get into power. And they are willing to unite for an emergency or to accept the results of an election because both are compromisers, in which they are also fundamentally alike.

Most people who know something about Freud's ideas take for granted an enduring antagonism between the conscious and unconscious parts of their minds, with the unconscious overwhelmingly more powerful. The conscious, or part of it, seems clever but weak. But one of Freud's great pessimistic sentences gives the conscious its rightful place. He said, "It is the same with life; it is not worth much, but it is all we have." We have our "conscious"; we do not have our "unconscious," and to some extent it has us.

But it is thinking in terms that are too passive to suppose that we, like icebergs, are swept along by the seven-eighths of our mind that is below the surface. The conscious can control, manage, or—what is even better—work in harmony with the unconscious. Of course there are times, in blind rage or in mental disease, when the conscious has no control. And there are neuroses in which conscious and unconscious forces fight each other to a standstill. But in many people the conscious and unconscious forces can work together.

This is recognized when it is said of a man that he "just naturally does what is sensible and right." Consciousness may be "clever" and in many ways comparatively weak, but it has the power of knowledge of the past and the possibilities of the future. With its strength it can even choose to accept an analysis in order to capture unconscious forces and bring them into its own camp. But all I want to indicate at this stage is that the conscious and unconscious need not always oppose each other. They can work together.

A sad experience is to find that many fine, sensitive, well-meaning people have to be placed farther down the line than their abilities seem to warrant because they are caught between the striving for perfection and the making of compromises.

The principle of perfection is to aim at a mark of 100 per cent; this aim suits the artist, the surgeon, the engineer. The principle of compromise is to aim at a passing mark or more, to get all out of a situation that is possible considering the time and the place. This suits the politician, the diplomat, the reporter.

There is a constructive side to the pursuit of the perfect as the artist strives in painting or music, as the athlete tries for a record, as conscientious people give their best efforts to their work and their families. But there is a French proverb that points to its destructive possibilities: "The best is often the enemy of the good."

Here is the perfectionist as revealed to the psychiatrist.

A man of forty had been brought up by stern parents who expected him always to get 100 per cent marks in school. At the age of nine he heard a preacher describe the unforgivable sin as blasphemy, and he thought he was guilty of it. He succeeded only when he went to college and there worked endlessly, punctiliously, in his specialty of chemistry. He began to teach but was so severe to all but the top boys in his classes that he was asked to resign. He was interested only in the "best," not in the "good" boys. Later, he expected perfection in his children's behavior and was so enraged when his three-year-old daughter walked across his "perfect" garden that he became confused and was taken to a psychiatric hospital.

But compromise also has two sides. At its most constructive it consists in driving a hard bargain with circumstances. A newspaper reporter is sent to cover a dangerous fire but is told that he must meet the closing time, the deadline for the last edition. He is obliged to send in an incomplete account because the fire doesn't observe the deadline. Similarly, the politician cannot afford to say, "I will not associate with certain people because it might lower my standards." Instead he will say, "To be elected, to bring better government to my city, I shall have to work with imperfect people under unfavorable conditions."

But he must know in what to compromise and in what to stand firm. It has been said that "half a loaf is better than no bread, but half a watch is no better than no watch." Being half honest, even in politics, is no better than not being honest at all.

There is actually a pursuit of perfection in hard compromise. "I'll do the best I can" implies that the very best would be none too good. A strong person can use perfection as a goal in large issues and yet compromise in minor matters.

Let us consider briefly some popular sayings which ignore the distinctions between big and little, between times when perfection is desirable and times when compromise will do.

"Anything worth doing at all is worth doing well." In one sense this is true, in another false. No individual should put all his purposes on the same level; if he does, he will be like the Caesar who, in the boy's translation, "mounted his horse and rode off in all directions at the same time." He will not be putting first things first. I think of an integrated person as one who puts the best that is in him into his main purpose, but gives less attention to secondary things. He takes up minor matters in a carefree, haphazard, desultory manner.

What are minor matters? For an engineer a minor interest may be singing, and for a Prime Minister or President, painting. We need minor matters that do not lie under the shadow of obligation, for if we try to do everything perfectly we can end by doing nothing.

An interesting case is that of a surgeon who put his best efforts into his exacting work, trying to perfect his techniques. When told that he needed relaxation he took up golf, and into golf he again put his best efforts, with the result that in a few years he was a state golf champion but had given up his surgical practice.

The desire to do well is so precious that it should not be wasted on "anything worth doing," but should be saved for the few main issues of life.

"Satan finds some mischief still for idle hands to do" is another one-sided maxim. It is false if it implies that Satan finds no mischief for busy hands like the nervous, reckless hands of Adolf Hitler. It is false if it implies that if you work all the time you are "good."

But in the Western world we have few spokesmen for the value of idleness, stillness, meditation, rest. The poet William Cowper, in a striking verse, wrote, " 'Tis thus the understanding takes repose in indolent vacuity of thought, and rests and is refreshed." Some of man's greatest achievements have been preceded by this "indolent vacuity of thought," but many leaders in our society find it impossible to accept this fact. The greatest investigator I have ever known, Walter B. Cannon, American physiologist, insisted that productiveness was favored by lack of pressure. "Leisure," he said, "is the Mother of Discovery." Modern industry also recognizes the value of occasional indolence by approving the coffee break, morning and afternoon, for workers in factories and business offices.

It is an old and silly saying that "cleanliness is next to godliness." If a man tried to be 100 per cent clean at all times he would be just as lost, just as futile, as he would be carrying a banner in a blizzard without proper equipment and at the wrong time, like the half-wit hero of "Excelsior." Not even an operating room can be kept immaculate. Too much scrubbing damages human tissues and opens the way to infection, defeating the purpose of washing.

Nineteenth-century literature produced many heroic characters who were really not very bright. In addition to the hero of "Excelsior," we have the boy who "stood on the burning deck whence all but him had fled," waiting for his dead father to tell him to get off the ship before it blew up!

Willingness to compromise with perfection provides an antidote for many disappointments. I have been struck with the unhappiness of students who have graduated second or third in a class, or even first, in contrast to the glowing smiles on the faces of those who came out near the bottom, grateful at getting through at all.

But a bishop who was asked to discuss the principle of compromise said, "Nonsense! When compromise comes in, principles go out." With this I disagree. Compromise is driving the hardest possible bargain with circumstance, taking the half-loaf when you are offered a quarter-loaf and want a whole loaf, taking second place cheerfully when you cannot come in first.

There is another saying which has its two sides. "It is later than you think." Its poor side is shown by the interpretation, "Work, never relax, there is no time to spare for play, rest, comedy." But the writer-philosopher Santayana said, "I have always found my chief pleasure and rest in doing nothing." * The Puritans, appalled at the dissipation, idleness, and frivolity of the courts of Charles I and II, became sober, hard-working, strong, honest, gloomy—and insufferable.

The Puritans and their fellow thinkers of our own time in all religions have failed to see that work and austerity on one side

* Laurence Dame, "Last Interview," *Harvard University Bulletin*, Nov. 10, 1956.

and play and joyousness on the other are complementary principles, to be used alternately to achieve the best and greatest results. We need neither the zealot nor the playboy, but a person who can work and then relax. For an example of industry gone wrong, there is the medical missionary who went to Africa on a six-year assignment. He thought that work was right and rest was wrong. He plunged into work night and day and soon was tired, achieving that irritability which goes so often with his kind of goodness. He soon made errors in judgment and was called home. It was some time before a substitute could be found to carry on his work. Meanwhile the people whom he was sent to help suffered; his unremitting labor was wasted, and they lost two years of medical care.

Of course, in all this discussion of perfection and compromise we have been involved in questions of conscience and what often appears to be conscience in the wrong place, as in the case of the boy on the burning deck. We now have to deal with the idea that there are two opposing principles in conscience, one constructive and the other destructive.

Chapter XII

CONFLICTS OF CONSCIENCE

IN AN EFFORT to simplify a complicated situation, and with apologies to Freud and to all psychoanalysts, I suggest that the mind has in it three divisions which are like the engine, the steering wheel, and the brake of an automobile. The engine— the instincts, the emotions, the desires—is built in at the start and has full sway in the baby, an attractive and appropriate sway. Much later the child stores up some information—a radiator burns, a pin is sharp—and begins to control itself by steering away from painful things. But a crowning control comes when the child builds a conscience to govern its instincts as a brake controls an engine. Then the baby's "I want what I want when I want it" changes to "I want it if it is right to have it."

Most children develop this conscience. But some do not, and there is no more impressive way to prove the value of an ethical self than to look at an intelligent man without one. It is a tragic sight. He has no inner struggle, no anxiety because he has no control and, therefore, nothing to cause conflict. That such a person has no interest in the past or future also shows that his is a baby's mind. And when you have a baby's mind in an intelligent, six-foot man you have destruction personified—a psychopath. There is nothing in such a person to fight the wish of the moment.

Here is an example of the psychopath. A man without a conscience was good-looking and intelligent. Dismissed from college because he forged a check, he was sent to a psychiatric hospital where he was an agreeable and companionable patient for a year; his politeness to older ladies was a model for young men. On leaving the hospital he found a good job, and for two weeks he impressed his employers as a possible future partner. One Saturday he was to receive his pay check for $60.00. At closing time on Friday he was given $15.00 to pay a debt to a firm in the neighborhood, but he went off with the money instead. As he had no conscience, it did not occur to him that he was stealing; as he could see only the present, it did not occur to him that he would lose $60.00 tomorrow. For forty years this "intelligent" man has repeated this behavior; he has lived in jail practically all the time, getting out only to forge another check. The psychopath, who is not further to be mentioned in this book, raises a question also not considered in these pages— "What is intelligence?" The young man described above measured 125 on the Binet scoring.

Now we return to the making of a conscience in most of us. One aspect—and an essential one—I can dispose of quickly. Let it be assumed that in most people there is from birth an "inner light" or that a "true conscience" can be built in by the church, parents, or substitutes for parents. This part of what is usually named conscience I do not pretend to discuss. What does interest me at this time is a babyish, distorted, disguised, accidental, cloudy, or destructive pseudo-conscience.

The mind grows from birth, and its growth is influenced by countless complicated forces from without, both by accident and design. Think, then, of the chances that inappropriate or destructive notions may be woven into the growing conscience. A child has a small vocabulary and cannot understand much of what is said to him. Sometimes he has poor teachers, amateurs in the art of training and feeding the growing mind no matter what academic degrees they may have. Sometimes he learns more from bad company than from good teachers.

Sometimes his parents themselves may not be sure what is right. Sometimes father says it is right and mother says it is wrong, or parents say one thing and act another. Accidental happenings, such as injuries, thunderstorms, death or illness of a parent, and other frightening experiences, may reinforce or nullify some lesson the child is learning.

Because so much of the ethical self is a precipitate of ideas received from parents at an early and partly unorganized age, it usually stands apart from the other areas of the mind as if it were another person, and it is mostly unconscious. The child is not critically aware of it, just as he is not consciously aware of the changes going on within his body except insofar as they give him physical pain or pleasure. And few parents can see beneath the surface to the alter ego which is growing in the child, even though they have much to do with shaping it.

How separate the conscience can be is illustrated by a personal experience, a convincing and disturbing dream in which I encountered my conscience face to face; it was not a pleasant meeting.

On an unseasonably warm March evening I went to sleep with all the windows wide open and with only my wife and myself in the house. I was awakened by great gusts of wind which rattled the window and blew the curtains in, but then I went to sleep again. I awoke a second time to see the rain pouring in. My wife was shutting the windows in the other rooms; all I did was to close the two windows nearest me. And I soon went to sleep again.

In the dream Mrs. Cummings, who had been a substitute mother to me and my wife during our college days, stood at the foot of my bed. She said to me, "Why didn't you get up and close those windows?" I replied, "I didn't think it was going to rain." She said, "Nonsense, Lee knew it." My next offer, "I was too sleepy," met with a stern reply. "Not any more sleepy than Lee."

Then I thought of a very clever and convincing excuse which would get me out of all blame. "Lee is a very unselfish person and likes to do things for others. I was giving her a chance to do a good deed." Mrs. Cummings looked at me sternly as she said, "That excuse is as poor as the others." She disappeared, and I woke up.

O wonderful, incorporated Voice! O clever, unscrupulous Me! How are we going to get along together? Here is a real and important conversation in the mind, the better part being projected into a parent-like other person. Yet I was really talking to myself, talking to the ethical self which disapproved and condemned the rest of me. Those who have encountered this Accuser in their dreams know, in some degree, what Freud means by the "super-ego."

The psychiatrist meets many patients who verbalize the separation of their conscience from the rest of their mind. A man convalescent after an alcoholic delirium lay quietly in bed, protesting that he was a sober individual who gave all his money to his wife every payday. But he asked me to remove a voice from a corner of the room which kept calling him a drunken, no-good sot. His conscience, his Voice, was projected about ten feet. The distance was necessary to the man, and the Voice had more truth and reality in it than the rest of his mind possessed. His conscience, standing apart from his mental and physical weaknesses, was appraising and accusing them.

In acknowledgment and recognition of this force within us, which is not quite ourselves, we sometimes say, "I would like to do this, but my conscience won't let me." Thus we admit the difference between the ego and the super-ego. If we mean well in general, we take orders or advice from our Accuser and try to do better. As I write this, on the day before President Eisenhower is to announce his decision about running for a second term, I see this quotation in the New Yorker from the Parisian newspaper Le Monde: "Who can predict what the worried conscience of Ike will dictate to him in their tête-à-tête?" The clear French phrase—head to head, face to face, a man and his conscience.

No one can be too conscientious, but many are too pseudo-conscientious or too scrupulous. The crowning development of the mind is the formation of an effective ethical control, but many fine people miss a high ranking in the line of normality because they have acquired or developed a shoddy substitute which is neither truly ethical nor effective. It is at best a "spurious conscience," if it is a conscience at all.

Shakespeare had it in mind, perhaps, when he wrote that "the web of our life is of a mingled yarn, good and ill together." If we may borrow Shakespeare's metaphor, we can think of the ethical self as a cloth. Into it have gone white threads, which are the constructive and "right" prohibitions and ideals of the parents, the church, and the community. These white threads might be called "conscience," and no one can have too many of them. But mixed with them are gray and black threads of mis- understanding, ignorance, errors, fears, "infantile survivals." These dark threads may make themselves so much a part of the whole pattern that they are given authority which they do not deserve.

A distinction needs to be made between matters of conscience and matters of conviction. A person may believe that the earth is flat or that two and two make five without suffering the emo- tional disturbances brought on by conflicts with conscience. All history tells us that men have managed to live happily and use- fully with innumerable ridiculous superstitions and false doc- trines.

But when a grown man feels—not believes—that he is doomed if he falls short of perfection, he is not really free to believe any- thing. He is a slave to his warped and undeveloped conscience, which was formed in childhood and never grew up. If he finds it almost a physical impossibility to do his work with dirty hands, he is not following any dictate of faith or reason. He is dominated by a conscience, a super-ego, which should have been discarded long ago. In that super-ego are such apparently trivial ideas that it is wrong to step on a crack, to rest, to be dirty. More important are the twin notions that it is fatal to fall short of perfection and wrong to acknowledge that inside one's con- forming self there are powerful and aggressive instincts and wishes. Such dark threads, as they infiltrate, distort, and tor-

ment in the name of conscience, are within the field of psychiatry.

It is not the psychiatrist's business to challenge his patient on
religion, politics, economics, or other matters of opinion. The
psychiatrist's task is to help his patient to resolve the emotional
conflicts which make him unhappy, confused, and inefficient.
While attempting to do so, he frequently encounters statements
like the following, which indicate that the trouble lies within a
pseudo-conscience formed in childhood.

"I was constantly told not to get dirty. Mother said dirtiness
was the worst sin." Serious disturbances, very difficult to cure,
may be caused by parental nagging about cleanliness.

"Don't–don't–don't!" Cautioned too much and too often, a
child can become so obsessed by formless fears that he wants to
stay at home, to retreat from life.

"Don't make a mistake." Inability to make adult decisions
may have its roots in this counsel of perfection in childhood.
"Father made me afraid of the wrath of God if I left a single
weed in the garden." The patient knows that the punishment
does not fit the crime, but now God's anger seems to follow him
everywhere.

"Father said sin and failure were the same thing." This patient won't try because he is afraid he may fail. Another, in
similar trouble, remembers that "if I got a 98 on my report my
parents asked why I didn't get 100."

These statements suggest a better adjective to describe the
conscience or super-ego or ethical self which has in it many
black and gray threads. The word is "immature." It is the immature conscience which overvalues the "don't's" of childhood,
which seeks safety in prohibitions, which readily sees faults,
which is perfectionistic.

An immature conscience thrives on vagueness; an adult conscience should be clear. If a man faces his known sins and repents
and atones, he can go on. A second-rate conscience is cautious;

a first-rate one should be daring and creative. The important thing is not how many weeds were left in the garden but how much of a crop was raised; not how many mistakes did this man make, but how far did he progress toward "spontaneous goodness." A patient once told me that "a craving for a clear conscience is highly egotistical." But Oscar Wilde said it first: "Conscience makes egoists of us all."

It is a pleasant digression from these considerations of the immature conscience to quote briefly from "The Creed of a Plain Man," written as one of his daily columns by the late Jay E. House, newspaperman and something of a philosopher.

> Our recipe for life is to keep busy and interested, and to be able to square ourself with ourself. The first requirement is easy enough; the second much more difficult. But the man who doesn't try to live up to the second gets nothing from life. No man ever derived an iota of satisfaction or a moment of happiness from being untruthful, dishonest, unfair, unkind or uncharitable. . . . We pay now and on the nail for acts which offend our sense of what is right and proper.

This is a formula for an adult conscience. Compare it, if you please, to the personal creed of a man whose conscience will not permit him to love or help his neighbor—or step on cracks in the pavement!

When many dark threads have been woven into a conscience, the result might be something like this. The person would be clean, successful, tense, tired from continual work, and in a chronic state of rather irritable goodness. But "the use of self-control," said Bertrand Russell, "is like the use of brakes on a train. It is useful when you find yourself going in the wrong direction, but merely harmful when the direction is right."

With a grown-up conscience an imperfect man, with inadequate preparation and at an inopportune time, can press on to help his fellow men. With a childish conscience he would never get a start. He would wait for perfect conditions, including clean hands. A host of little "don't's" would get in the way of the large issues. Incidentally, there have been dirty saints who made a special virtue of their dirtiness and sinners who kept themselves scrupulously clean and immaculately clothed.

But it is in the production of a feeling of guilt that the immature conscience really triumphs. If you have absolute standards and you are a human being, you cannot live up to those standards and you are forever guilty. Some of the most innocent people I know are weighted down by guilt and cannot explain why. They cannot come face to face with their sins. They see a shadow, a ghost, an unknown horror, an infantile survival. They would give all they have to be able to repent, but they don't know of what to repent. They can see only a rolling, shifting cloud; they try to imagine what sin of theirs is behind it; they are filled with anxiety; they are neurotic.

Without knowing how or why, they develop bodily pains. If they are lucky enough to break an arm, they have something definite and reassuring to show in a visible cast and sling. This they may proudly accept as the punishment for their secret offenses, as though the ailments of the body could compensate for the sins of the soul. More often they shift the confusion of their conscience to the broken limb and are reasonably happy until it is well again.

Who are the "they" I have been talking about? Among them are many of our best people, the most sensitive, the responsibility takers, the chairmen of committees, the leaders in good causes. We need the high ideals such leaders bring to us; we need cautions. Even emphasis on the value of work has its good points, and cleanliness is not objectionable unless carried too far—while it is not next to godliness, it is a pleasant social grace. But these good people might profitably reflect on something written by Robert Louis Stevenson: "The conscience has morbid sensibilities; it must be employed but not indulged, like the imagination or the stomach."

What one wishes for the responsibility takers, the fine people we all know, is the discovery of a new world of things which are morally neutral. Such things as air, beauty, the color of a sunset, food, humor, laughter, music, play, rest, sports, zest. By themselves they carry no ethical burden. From time to time they can be put into the field of morals, but in and of themselves they offer inspiration, happiness, and relief from "moral tentacles." They bring the haphazard joys of the amateur, for the amateur is not obsessed by the idea that only perfection is worthwhile. He is happy in the work he is doing, not possessed and persecuted by it.

All these considerations lead to one main conclusion. Psychiatrists, including psychoanalysts, have come to believe that no mental health is possible without a conscience, which to them is a third side of growth—and a crowning side. Without a conscience, and the constructive things which that conscience can learn, there is only the shell of a human being "with no health in him." But the adjectives that describe this conscience should be "constructive, daring, forward-looking, happy, affirmative, productive."

The late Austin Riggs spoke up for a four-way conscience that would help a man to *work* hard (forgetting play), *play* hard (forgetting work), *rest* well (forgetting play and work), and *worship*. These add up to an affirmative conscience which can help a man to live "happily, triumphantly, victoriously, and creatively."

Chapter XIII

THE DOWNWARD DRIFT

IT HAS BEEN SAID several times that the place of any individual in
the line of the normal, more or less, is not fixed or permanent.
Changes for the better or worse are sometimes sudden and
dramatic; more often there is a slow improvement or decline.
Some persons shift back and forth in the line, up today and
down tomorrow, and probably up again a few days later.

There are some massive downward pulls with which the world
of today is painfully familiar. They are outside the individual;
he is not personally responsible for them, yet they press heavily
upon him. Totalitarianism, as a philosophy and mode of government, by definition degrades the individuals who live under its
iron law. They cannot be independent; they can only conform
and obey, and suffer or die for disobedience. It is not a cliché
to say that totalitarianism denies and destroys the dignity and
integrity of the individual. That is its plan and purpose.

The threat of total war has the same effect. It diminishes our
hope for the future, our long distance goal. An associated catas-
trophe would be the destruction of man's capacity to reproduce
and perpetuate his kind. He would be left without a future for
which to prepare, work, and plan. Little is worth anything today
if nothing will be worth anything tomorrow. The outcome is
chaos, both for the individual and for society.

The slums which are the cancer sores of great cities press
heavily on all who live in their shabby, crowded homes. Sordid
surroundings and bad company drag them down. So does the
ugliness of their environment; so does the smog which so often
matches the drab monotony of their lives.

Yet we know that some persons can rise above these generally harmful influences. Heroic individuals managed to keep their spirits free under the bondage of Hitlerism. There are free men still behind the thickest Iron Curtain. History tells of many men and women who held their own against enormous pressures and of others who have kept hope alive in the world's darkest hours. We remember the words of Portia at the end of Shakespeare's *The Merchant of Venice:* "How far that little candle throws its beams! So shines a good deed in a naughty world."

Since some men can be free against the greatest outer odds, the study of downward pulls *inside* the individual are important. What are they, and how can we resist them?

In this connection it helps us to think of the line of human beings as if it were on a long, steep hill. Those at the upper end can slide down rather easily. Those at the lower end must climb up, and it may take unusual character, courage, and determination to do so. But sliding down is easy.

A force that is something like gravity tends to pull everyone down the line. It is a clinging to the familiar, a fear of the unknown, an embrace of nirvana, sleep, the easy way. Easy for the moment, at least, though it may mean hardship in the long run. It is a tendency to escape responsibilities, problems, troubles, the brutal facts and injustices of life by running away from them—and there are many ways to run and many places to run away to.

We prefer to run away to a place which is more pleasant and peaceful than the one in which we are. At least, we think or hope it will be. The downward pull, therefore, uses the attractiveness of sleep, of rest, of comfort, of flight to far places.

What happens if we yield to these sirens' songs and attractive temptations? We may find the answer by listening to our teachers, the mental patients who drift downward or are dragged down to lower levels on the line. They say that their "last state is worse than the first." The tendency to escape under fire or pressure is by no means a monopoly of the mental patient, for we all have our drifting moments. So we should readily recognize the "escape mechanisms" and excuses of the mental patient as our own.

A simple way to escape is to close one's eyes to try to make trouble vanish. This is why many men with crippling neuroses repeat over and over, "There is nothing wrong with me," "I have no problem." Many allegedly normal people do much the same thing. Queen Victoria, for many years after her husband's death, had a can of hot water and his evening clothes brought to his room every evening. In this way she denied the fact of his death.

Fond parents and worried relatives may also try to run away from trouble by closing their eyes and pretending it isn't there. A mother came from Pittsburgh to Philadelphia to consult me at the hospital. She said, "There is nothing the matter with my daughter. There can't be anything the matter, because she is my daughter." I simply said, "It is a long trip from Pittsburgh," and then she described her daughter's illness, having first eased her mind by denying its existence.

Almost as simple as closing one's eyes is going to bed. Sometimes we do so logically and sensibly, planning to be in better shape to solve a problem or deal with difficulties after a good night's sleep. But the neurotic goes to bed because he is running away from realities, not getting ready to meet them.

A man of thirty suddenly stopped work and went to bed. His wife, to meet this difficulty and make her husband return to work, went to bed for six months. Their daughter retreated to bed for six months when her own husband failed to be promoted. Their son retired for eighteen years from a successful business to lead a "dressing-gown life" in bed or pacing about the room. If you remain in bed you conventionally attract sympathy, you escape obligations, and you also punish those who must wait on you.

Taking to bed is tied up with the downward pulls of different physical illnesses. It is also tied up with taking to the South Seas

or some other refuge from things as they are. In the movie
Mutiny on the Bounty millions saw the hero lying on a soft,
sunny beach, reaching up lazily for the fruit of a tree whose
branches bent down to him. In sickness, too, a man can find in
bed a soft spot "with a good climate," and he can reach up for
food as his wife or nurse bends down to him with a tray.

Retreat into bed to escape the troubles of our civilization is
matched by more active and desperate escapes into geography.

Three distinguished authors, Vincent Sheehan, Russell Maloney, and Negley Farson, have described their own flights from
disappointments to primitive retreats, from crowded cities of
Christian civilization to the Mohammedan deserts. The three
books from which I quote should be on the shelves of everyone
interested in the way minds work.

Sheehan, in *Personal Reminiscences*, says, "My youth was
spent in flight. . . . Mother's death made college unbearable."
He fled from Chicago to New York, Paris, Rome, Madrid; to
Tangier and the desert; to Persia and the desert; to China,
London, the Holy Land and its desert.

Maloney, son of an Irish Catholic father who lived in Mexico
and a Christian Scientist mother who came from Virginia, was
held behind barbed wire in a German prison camp from his
seventeenth to twenty-first year. He brought away a fear of open
spaces and a distrust of European civilization. He ran to Morocco
and the desert; then to Poland, Russia, Hungary, Canada, Swit-
zerland, France. He also fled into alcoholism. His own account of
his flight and his redemption makes *New Armour for Old* a remarkable book. It raises the question of how many Americans
have ever longed for "the blessed simplicity and soothing fatal-
ism of the Moslem."

A third story of inner unrest and geographical flight is told
by Negley Farson in *The Way of a Transgressor*. His itinerary
was England, Norway, Russia, Egypt and the desert; two years
of utter isolation on a lake in British Columbia followed by restless wanderings to Chicago, mid-Europe, Turkey, India, Spain,

Poland. "When I sailed from America the first time I felt I was running away from things I ought to face. Perhaps what I had been looking for was a new set of values."

Add the strange story of Lawrence of Arabia and his flight into desert spaces, and you have a galaxy. All its stars give us a sympathetic understanding of the common longings of the common mind.

We turn back briefly to Mary Tree and her flight from bleakness and a sadistic husband into delusion and hallucination. It was not possible for a married woman without funds to arrange to go around the world, but she could run away to the nearest park. The remainder of the trip she took cheaply and easily in her imagination, a flight into psychosis instead of the deserts.

The neurotic drinker is also a drifter, running away from reality. One has told me, "Alcohol stands between me and some awful memories." Some find in liquor an escape from boredom, which is usually the fault of themselves, not their environment. Some find release from dissatisfaction with themselves. Yet to most people it is puzzling that certain drinkers always drink too much; they don't stop until they get into trouble or pass out. The author Maloney, quoted above, fled from his fears either into the deserts or into alcohol. But he could afford to travel, as others cannot. For many men it is easier to take a drink than to organize themselves to visit the strange and lonely corners of the world.

Death is the final escape for some. Hamlet dallied with the idea. "To die, to sleep; and by a sleep to say we end the heartache and the thousand natural shocks that flesh is heir to, 'tis a consummation devoutly to be wished." Drinkers often reach this final consummation; they are subconsciously seeking it while they drink. Alcoholism, for them, is a way station on the road of escape into death.

Alcoholic passing out, whether or not it is imitation of death, is typical of the easy way. It blots out the hideous past and the hopeless future; it blots out conscience and responsibilities; it brings dependence and childishness, as do other drugs—and sleep.

All the men who sought the deserts and distant lands suggested, among other things, the flight into activity. Among less gifted people it is expressed in this way: "I must fill every waking moment with engagements, shopping, committee meetings. I don't dare to sit down and think." Much of the customary thinking of the Western world shelters and excuses those who flee into overactivity. They accept the idea that "you are good if you work hard." In the mental patient the flight into overactivity may take other physical forms. In the middle of an excitement, a woman who had never stopped talking and moving for weeks suddenly interrupted her ceaseless activity to stare down at the floor with a look of horror on her face, as though gazing into the depths. Then she jerked herself up and began to dance and jest and sing.

Sometimes the downward drift is revealed as an easy escape into childishness and dependence. Early in 1929, Mr. G. plunged into the stock market and into real estate. In April he became depressed, and against the advice of his wife, his banker, and his lawyers he sold out everything he had and put all his money into government bonds. Though he saved all his money while his advisers lost all theirs, he retired still further from grown-up responsibilities by becoming a baby. His wife and a nurse had to feed him by spoon, bathe him, take him to the toilet, and, in lieu of a baby carriage, wheel him in a rolling chair.

Professor K., at thirty-six, had risen to the top of his department and was to be made vice-president of a great university, with increased responsibilities. He had a "nervous breakdown." For the remainder of a long life he did the work of a ten-year-old boy, mowing the lawn, doing simple errands, reading only the weekly newspaper which printed the gossip of the town.

A charming and dangerous habit of mind is daydreaming. It is easy and childlike; it offers rest and comfort and escape. I quote from a story, "Star of Destiny," by Clifford Raymond, which appeared in the *Saturday Evening Post:* *

"Thus Oscar danced with life and death. He wrote many things which he did not put down on paper; wrote them as he walked, or sat at his desk . . . or smoking by the stove before he went home on a winter night.

The wedding of our brilliant fellow citizen, Mr. Oscar Storm, to Miss Sally Hughes, president of the Central City Bank, was solemnized last night. The bride was ravishing in a creation by Mlle. Celeste, of E. Main St., and was given away by her father. The bridegroom wore the conventional black. The impressive ring ceremony was followed. After the ceremony the happy pair departed for the East, where Mr. Storm is supervising several dramatic productions of his works.

"That was Oscar. He could live a whole life walking the street and writing headlines.

Oscar Storm, Great American Playwright, Revisits Native City.

Oscar Storm, Native of this City, Marries Miss Sally Hughes in Paris.

Oscar Storm, Author of The Whirlwind, The Crucible and Other Great Plays of American Life, Marries Miss Sally Hughes in New York.

"Oscar did not leave any drop in the cup untasted:

The body of Oscar Storm, distinguished son of this City, will lie in state at the city hall tomorrow. The Third Infantry will meet the funeral train tonight. It was Mr. Storm's wish to be buried in Greenleaf Cemetery, where his wife, who was Miss Sally Hughes, lies buried. Mr. Storm survived her only a month. Their union was ideal in life and continues after death. Many bequests to charity.

* January 19, 1924.

"Sometimes Oscar was so engrossed in writing headlines and stories as he walked along that he completely passed out of reality for blocks."

After this engaging fantasy in a normal young man who did not allow dreams to interfere with his work, look at this distressing rejection of daydreaming in this religious (?) woman. "I cannot go to hear the Christmas carols because so many of them are founded on fiction." But what if they are? Even good King Wenceslaus is a harmless, agreeable fiction. So is the fiction that it is fun to ride in a one-hoss open sleigh on a bitter cold night. Few who sing about it really want to do it any more than they really yearn for a "white Christmas."

Daydreaming can be good or bad. It can exercise the imagination and smooth rough corners in life, but it is destructive when it offers an easy way out of work and obligations. To live constructively people must do hard thinking, based on facts, controlled by facts, scientific, tied to the ground of reality. The daydreamer floats along tied to nothing. John, for example, at the age of fourteen, is daydreaming to an alarming extent. For hours in the evening he paces up and down in his room having soldierly adventures. Yet he is tenth out of 110 in his class, and he has a lively athletic interest. I think that he will come out well, in time.

A distinguished writer, Storm Jameson, says in *No Time Like the Present*, "I never told anyone what I was thinking. I now think the daydreams of imaginative children are a dangerous experiment. They become with time a corrosive habit that persists and holds the mind back from the direct awareness of reality. Rawness and harshness offend and the mind turns to feed itself on dreams."

None show the full results of this escape from life so well as schizophrenic patients.

A stubborn, courageous little girl was deeply devoted to her father. She did not get along well with children of her own age and soon was daydreaming to a marked extent. At a boarding school and later at college she had crushes on other girls. She set aside definite hours each evening for daydreaming. Her father's death was a shock which increased the daydreams until they were "more interesting than reality." But at nineteen she said that the dreams stopped and were replaced by the following "real" happenings. She received divine messages; she was pregnant from an enema. The change at nineteen was like the change from water to ice, a metamorphosis which has been mentioned before. It indicates that a bad habit has become a fixed psychosis.

It may be that feelings of inferiority are almost universal in human beings because they have such a long childhood. There are so many years in which they are small and weak, living in a world of larger and stronger persons. Later they try to fortify their self-esteem by talking bigger than they are. This kind of thing is called overcompensation, and it is a downward pull or drift because it serves only to make the braggart more conscious of his inferiority.

Thus a tiny, rosy-cheeked boy once broke down and cried, "I am so small I could run around on the brim of your hat." But he tried to avoid facing reality by saying, "I am as good as Dempsey," and by hitting every boy he met—with disastrous consequences to himself.

You may remember a young man whom I used as an example of the utmost in aggression. For eighteen years he was gentle and imposed upon, but for the next eighteen he attacked everyone he saw and he killed one man. This, too, is the outcome of overcompensation.

A parallel case appeared in a newspaper. A boy of fourteen had a sissy feeling because he was made to wash dishes and dust furniture. So he killed an eleven-year-old friend "to assert his superiority."

Here is what a mental patient said of himself: "I am a General, a millionaire, and I play some tennis." He had been a failure as a private in the militia; he had failed in business; but he was a tennis champion. He did not need to overstate his strong point, the one thing in which he excelled, but he exaggerated the ones in which he was a failure. This is a commonplace weakness, for many of us make mountains out of our molehills in this fashion. For example, we allow acquaintances to think we are experts in sports, handicrafts, and hobbies, though we know very well we are rank amateurs. We may be "name-droppers," hinting that we are on intimate terms with prominent people whom we have met only once and who have completely forgotten us. If this sort of thing becomes a habit, a man should warn himself that he is drifting, and in the wrong direction.

Chapter XIV

MORE DOWNWARD DRIFT

IT IS TIME to take another deep breath before plunging in to consider realistically and rudely some more of our delicate, fanciful, and ingenious methods of lulling ourselves into easy ways and a lower position in the line.

If some intolerable thing inside you hurts after all ordinary efforts to get rid of it; if, in Thornton Wilder's words, you have "lost hope, if you find you are not as good as you thought you were, if you have done something wrong and can't undo it," then you can fall ill and for the moment find some relief. Illness, therefore, can be an excuse for failure, an explanation, an alibi, a subtle reproach to critics who "do not understand." Again, it is an escape downward from unpleasant facts and painful realities.

A woman with an intolerable depression, moaning and pacing the room, fell in the bathtub and broke her arm. When she displayed the visible cast—which she cuddled as if it were a baby—she was calm. When the cast was gone and the arm healed, she returned to her wailing and restlessness.

Olive was a young woman who found herself engaged to the wrong man. She could see no way to break the engagement; she felt caught, imprisoned in a cage. Suddenly she was confused and excited and was sent to a mental hospital. Her fiancé set her free. Soon she recovered completely and married a man about whom she had no doubts.

Dr. Francis Braceland told me of a man hemmed in by three conditions which he could not bear. The first was a night job; he desperately wanted to work in the day. The second was a court order forcing him to pay for the support of a baby which he claimed was not his; his former girl friend and the judge claimed otherwise. The third was pressure from another girl who insisted that he marry her soon. The man came to the hospital with severe pains in the head and abdomen and was studied in several departments for a year before he was referred to Dr. Braceland, who found that by stepping down into illness this patient had rid himself of these three unbearable conditions. He did not have to work at night, he could not pay for the child's support, and he could not marry.

Retreat into illness can be a superficial affair designed to avoid some minor discomfort. It is altogether too well advertised. I recall one episode in the well-known "Mr. & Mrs." comic strip of Sunday morning, May 10, 1947. Mr. Green remains in bed, complaining of lack of appetite but eating a huge breakfast, while his wife telephones to the office that he is still "resting comfortably."

A totalitarian government tries to handle this matter in a typically bureaucratic way. In the factories of East Germany, "not more than six employees may be off sick at the same time."

A splendid sentence on this subject comes from Adler. "He says 'no' to life with his sinus, his heart, his skin or any other organ which happens to be the loud speaker of his soul." Imagined illness, which is sometimes very real to the patient, is just that—saying "no" to life.

"Doctor, I have some hard decisions to make," one patient said. "I hope that your examination will find something wrong with every gland in my body and relieve me of some of the heavy responsibility that weighs on me."

The advantages of illness were known long ago. Ever since children were first sent to school they have been artists in illness. Every weekday thousands of children all over the country, fearful of what will happen in school or on the way to it, come down with nausea or headaches in ingenious variations at about 8:30 A.M.; and at 9:30 remarkable recoveries begin.

A nice double effort to get rid of some inner conflict was shown me by a Mrs. A. First she blamed other people. One of her doctors was dishonest, the other mistaken, her minister was a liar, her neighbors hypocrites, and her nurse a gossipmonger. All these efforts to push her inner trouble onto other people were followed by attempts to transfer it to her body. So she had headaches, palpitation of the heart, cancer (?), was treated by high colonics, drainage of gallbladder, urinary bladder, and antrum, and x-rays of the thyroid. For a time she was "nearly blind," and "blood tests showed that the pituitary was not functioning." Her complaints—those against doctors evidently pretty well justified—and her attention to bodily symptoms and their treatments kept her from facing squarely the fears that were in her. But the fears were still there.

Accidental injuries are sometimes a preferred form of illness, perhaps because they are so dramatic. One girl had an intolerable feeling that she was not so pretty or able as her sister. At first she complained of gallbladder, then tonsils, then uterus. She was in pain all day, restless and discontented. Then she fell and had a compound fracture of an arm. Like a patient described above, she was then pleased and calm; all her digestive symptoms and abdominal pains disappeared.

But the distance between nervous patients and ordinary people in this respect is not great. If there is anything about which people are more emotional, capricious, fussy, and unreasonable than they are about their diets, I don't know what it is. Men insist that their food likes and dislikes be catered to. Many women regard food as a chore which is continually interrupting the day or as a source of unwanted weight, and I am told that most of the women of this country are dieting, more or less successfully.

Children have found that they can get more attention by refusing to eat than in any other way. Nowadays they pick their foods according to the emotions aroused by their favorite radio or television heroes. I take my hat off to the University of

Pennsylvania athletic coach who gave a new breakfast cereal this recommendation: "Milk is a very nutritious food, and it loses none of its great value if used with So-and-So's breakfast flakes."

Advertising and nervousness have built up a fantastic superstructure of food fads, special diets which cater only to whims, and some cults which are almost food religions.

When I hear people talking of the dreadful effects which have followed the eating of food which was not properly prepared and cooked, I recall a woman who swallowed a toothbrush. The handle was hard, dense bone, probably well seasoned before it was turned into a toothbrush handle. The x-rays showed that the bone was broken into little pieces as it went through the digestive juices; after that it disappeared. The human mouth and stomach, like some human minds, can swallow almost anything and survive.

A story of feeding difficulties from birth was obtained and verified in the case of a girl whose mother's main object in life was, and still is, to feed her. The child bit and scratched during early breast feeding. Later she refused milk from a bottle. A description of her feeding difficulties is taken from hospital records made when the child was two years old. She grew up on a limited diet; she broke any milk bottle that she could find; she refused to come to family meals and ate by herself irregularly. She bit and scratched other children, and for this reason she was dismissed from school.

At a hospital school she gained in ability to get on with people, but she became emaciated unless forced to eat. Her mother preferred the other side of the dilemma and placed her in a mental hospital where she was tube-fed and gained thirty pounds. She became deluded and would hold one position for hours. She could not be well nourished and well behaved at the same time!

Turning now to patients whom the psychiatrist would call neurotic, we find that many of them have been referred to him by an internist or pediatrician. And in these cases the digestive symptom, as a symbol of mental illness, stands out clearly.

A woman said to me, "I struggle between a feeling of being dirty and a reluctance to brush my teeth or go near a dentist. As an infant I nearly starved because I would not take milk. Now I am babyish; I can't talk."

A college girl had been coaxed to eat as a baby. At eight, when her curls were cut off, she had severe diarrhea. In college she read cookbooks all day and had to supervise the preparation of her own meals. She became emaciated, not because she didn't have good food to eat, but because something inside her fought against eating and enjoying it.

The conversion of open or concealed emotion into physical symptoms is favored by a special nervous system which quickly responds to certain mental conditions. Dr. Walter B. Cannon founded the science of gastroenterology when, in the earliest days of the fluoroscope, he was watching the churning of the stomach of a comfortable cat, purring after a good meal. A dog happened to bark outside the window, and all the churning and digestion stopped. The cat did not stop them, but her sympathetic nervous system did. Human beings can get constipation, diarrhea, nausea, and even ulcers in the same way and for the same reason.

A poet or songwriter put a lot of romance and emotion into the repeated statement that "my heart stood still." He would have been more exact if he had said, "My stomach and intestines stood still."

The advantages of organic illnesses are sometimes appreciated. Here is what was said by a hard-working conscientious university president who has been quoted before.

"I was anxious to help the students. I took a personal interest in each of them, but there were so many of them! Also the alumni were always demanding my time to speak at dinners and to keep up a good football team. The faculty—each one was a specialist who could see only his own field. My wife—well, she is very conscientious, full of good works, and she didn't want me to slight anything. So a year ago I came down with a coronary occlusion, and since then I've had the time of my life. During four months in the hospital and six months of convalescence I could relax. I read all the books I hadn't had time for up to then. I made pleasant friends who asked nothing of me. I could think undisturbed. No responsibilities! Not even my wife, not even my own conscience thought of criticizing me in my days of rest. Always there was the good old coronary occlusion standing watch over my happiness."

This reminds me that the wish to fall ill, the need to fall ill, does deserve a few kind words, even though it is a backward step or downward drift. It supports many doctors. It protects some school children. It brings some rest to the weary and some peace to the overconscientious. It soothes some anxiety in a fear-ridden world.

Many of the backward pulls which I have talked about have been simple enough. A brilliant doctor used to say, "All mental hygiene is an elaboration of the obvious," and often this is too true. But some surrenders to the downward drift take a less obvious or familiar form. For instance, to escape from life by appealing to conscience or to the fringes of conscience is to maneuver back of a more opaque screen where reality can't reach us and our real obligations won't bother us. One way of getting out of hard work is to insist on perfect conditions, absolute quiet, absolute order on the desk, absolute perfection in the tools. And if you spend all your time on the first of ten duties or the first of ten questions on an examination paper, then you may persuade yourself that you have an excuse for leaving nine undone.

You "hitch your wagon to a star," but then you wait until the star comes along. The waiting is not idle—you fuss, make notes, polish the tools, keep busy preparing. Here is a clear retreat from work and reality. If anyone criticizes you, you reply, "Look at my high ideals. I am awaiting the perfect opportunity to do a perfect job."

Now we come to another simple and devastating pull downward, away from the great realities of living. It is rationalizing, making ourselves out to be more reasonable than we are, deciding a matter by emotion and then rushing up reasons to defend the decision.

"I love my child." If this statement could end with the period it would be constructive. But if this follows—". . . because he is the best and brightest boy in the neighborhood"—these unnecessary reasons are sure to bring trouble to the boy, his playmates, and his teachers.

No one has described rationalization better than William James did sixty years ago. "The drunkard drinks because it is Christmas, because it is cold, because a drink will stimulate him to a more powerful resolution to abstain. He brings forward every reason except that he is a drunkard."

A British critic, commenting on the opening performance of an American actress, said, "She has a voice like a ventriloquist's doll." Coming upon the critic in a crowded lunchroom, the actress slapped his face "to vindicate American womanhood." This is rationalizing with a vengeance!

Here are other examples of rationalization from the psychiatrist's notebook.

A student says, "I failed in history and the Bible; they were too silly to study." A cynic was thinking of this important downward pull when he said, "Education is valuable because it enables you to explain and justify your prejudices."

All people make decisions because of strong instincts and emotions, and then pay homage to the intellect by finding reasons to justify those decisions. And so all along the line, rationalization confuses issues, confirms our prejudices, adds to the world's troubles, and drags us downward. It ought to be easy, then, for all people to see how mental patients think under strong and persistent emotion. They do the same as we do, only more so.

"I am sad and hopeless; nothing helps. I pray, but there is no response. Why? Not because there is no God, but because I am worthless and sinful."

At times most people, hating to acknowledge some fault in themselves, instinctively locate the fault in someone else. They kill two birds with one stone by separating the unbearable thing from the rest of their minds and by pushing it onto someone else, where it can be properly condemned.

In this way a little girl faced an intolerable shame when, as hockey goalie for her school, she knocked the puck into her own net and scored a winning point for the other team. She slammed her stick to the ground, shrieking, "Why can't you play better than that? You are the worst bunch of players I ever saw!"

This news item appeared in a daily paper in England some years ago:

A Mrs. A. M. Huggett, who insulted a girl dressed in beach pyjamas, was fined 10s. by the Eastbourne Magistrates yesterday for disorderly conduct. The girl said that when she was walking along the front in beach pyjamas Mrs. Huggett used offensive language towards her, and said: "Why don't you go home and get dressed, you brazen hussy?" Mrs. Huggett, in evidence, said the pyjamas offended her eyes, as they did the eyes of thousands of other people. She objected to people coming to Eastbourne dressed in that way. She admitted that she called Miss Ashford "a brazen hussy." The Chief Constable having informed the Magistrates that Mrs. Huggett was a woman of dirty habits and "a disgrace to the town," the Chairman, remarking that she was no attraction to Eastbourne and had yet the audacity to talk to Miss Ashford in the way she had done, fined her as stated. . . .

A well-known comedian is quoted as saying, "The lamppost got in the way of my car." It was the lamppost's fault, not the comedian's. A wife said to her husband, "Don't drink another cocktail—your face is getting blurry." And an unhappy patient said, "I keep hearing people going out of their way to make jeering remarks."

And now comes prejudice, about the worst down-puller of them all. I am glad that the word is not found in a dictionary of psychiatric terms; in psychiatry it is divided into its components of projection, rationalization, overcompensation, and other mechanisms of deceit and destruction. Prejudice is a complicated and insidious thing; it is almost the same thing as neurosis; it is a sister of delusion and far more dangerous. Anatole France shows its ability to come in at the back door when it is pushed out the front. "He flattered himself that he had no prejudices and this pretention itself is a very great prejudice." And a student once told me, "I have a prejudice against students who have prejudices."

Always there are emotion and judgment, followed—not preceded—by reasoning. A city council passed an ordinance and then asked for a debate on the subject. Adlai Stevenson quoted a lawyer who said in his address to a jury, "Gentlemen, these are the *conclusions* on which I base all my *facts*." Voltaire pointed out that "it is so difficult to think; that is why we prefer to pass judgments." Prejudices save a lot of thinking about one's prejudices—just blame the other fellow.

A delightful essayist, the late Samuel M. Crothers, had this to say in *The Pardoner's Wallet:* *

The Forbidden City [of the mind] is inhabited not by orderly citizens under the rule of Reason, but by a lawless crowd known as the Prejudices—who have a knack of living without any visible means of support.

A man is seldom offended by an attack on his reasoned judgments. They are supported by evidence and can shift for themselves. Not so with a prejudice. It is his own. He is perhaps its only defense against the facts.

There are different kinds of people with prejudice. At one extreme stand those in whom lies great hatred—for whom hatred is a natural need and who, perhaps, adopt prejudice as an

* Houghton Mifflin Co., Boston, 1905, pp. 47 and 80.

outlet instead of becoming criminal. In such people there is a tremendous narrowing of thought, feeling, imagination; their Forbidden Cities are large and have high walls to keep out reason. They are potential Hitlers, and only force prevails against them.

Next come people also deeply prejudiced, not so much because of an inner need but because of the customs, traditions, and culture in which they are brought up. They have absorbed the community attitude. When such people read of events which go against their usual ideas, or when they move to a different community, they often begin to feel uneasy. Such people can and do change attitudes, although change is difficult at first. Outsiders would do well to look to their own prejudgments before casting aspersions on this type of inherited bigotry. And it is wise not to go too far in supporting a minority or a weaker group merely to avoid the accusation of prejudice. Not everyone in such a minority is praiseworthy.

And last come the rest of us with our random prejudices, sometimes many and deep, sometimes few and trivial. These are the people who need and may respond, like the second group, to efforts to help them. Their prejudices are built up by accident, often in early childhood. Sometimes their emotional judgments in favor of their own family, school, or nation are harmless enough. To be *for* something is better than being against. But harm comes from shutting out, from losing sight of an individual in a group, from isolation, from lagging behind the times.

In Chapter XVII we will discuss some remedies which may mitigate or abolish prejudice. Here we shall only mention a few of the contrasting words we use when we think of ourselves and when we think of the same attitudes in other people. "I am determined—you are obstinate." "He is pigheaded—I have a strong mind." "I have faith—you have a prejudice." "I have ideas—he has delusions." *We* are right, in our town, in our families, and in our ways that have come down to us from our fathers. *You* from another town, keep out of this! *They* are wrong—those foreigners with strange ways and ideas new to us, who don't know enough to speak English as we do!

The dictionary definition of prejudice is that it is "a mental decision based on grounds other than reason." This brings up an interesting question. How many of our decisions in courtship and marriage, in family life, in politics and religion, are based on reason? If reason entered into a political campaign, would there be any campaign left?

A rather sad remark was made by Benjamin Franklin when he was discussing the making of our Consitution. "When you assemble a number of men to have advantage of their joint wisdom, you inevitably assemble with those men all their prejudices, their passions and their selfish views." This still stands as a commentary on the American Congress, the British Houses of Parliament, and any other chamber of representative government.

Prejudice is a universal weakness and problem, of course, though in different ways different countries are trying to deal with it. I am grateful to the King of Denmark for one sentence which referred to a special prejudice and suggested a cure for it. When asked by a Nazi general how the Danes managed the Jewish danger and problem he replied, "We don't have any danger or problem because we don't think the Jews are any better than we are." No better, and by the same token no worse.

After listening to projections of faults onto other people, the words of a Southern spiritual come gracefully and gratefully to the ear.

"It's not my brother but it's me, O Lord, standing in the need of prayer."

Repression, or the unconscious pushing of an act or fantasy out of awareness and memory, is so important and so complicated that it should be included in this discussion of the down-pulling influences or drifts. It usually is a pull downward because there is evidence that the thing repressed is not out of mind, but only out of consciousness. This suggests, by the way, the fallacy of another phrase—"out of sight, out of mind." Repression also implies a certain disunity, wasted energy, inappropriate action, all tending to drag the mind downward.

There is a connection with the downward pulls mentioned earlier. When an idea unbearable to a person is projected into someone else it is in a double sense "out" of one's own mind. When the unbearable becomes a physical pain it is also "out." When it is a compulsion it is changed and no longer recognizable as the terrible thing it really is. We naturally use whatever method comes to hand to get a temporary relief from responsibility, hard work, threatened danger, or guilt. And in our use of any method—except deliberate lying and cheating—there is something of the unconscious.

Is this all about the vital part repression plays in human life? Yes, for the intelligent reader, the engineer, the teacher, the chemist, the banker, No, for the psychiatrist and the analyst, and the novelist or poet.

Booth Tarkington, in his *Image of Josephine,* said:

> Bailey Fount didn't know himself to be as a matter of course Bailey Fount; he didn't seem to be just one person. It was as if within him were unreliable strangers who couldn't be trusted to say the right, ordinary things, but might at any moment become irresponsible, babble, startle listeners. He had carefully to think beforehand of every word he was going to say, almost of every movement before he made it. He didn't feel himself to be a natural part of human kind; he felt out of the herd, disqualified for fellowship, and just to shake hands with anybody seemed a false pretense. Apparently he was made of many separate pieces that weren't holding together, like a watch that couldn't keep time any more, and what's a watch for? *

In the following case is a clear example of repression. A little girl of four or five, wandering into her parents' room at night, saw something of sexual intercourse, something frightening, puzzling,

---

* From: *Image of Josephine* by Booth Tarkington. Copyright 1945 by Booth Tarkington, reprinted by permission of Doubleday and Company, Inc. Courtesy of Curtis Brown, Ltd., New York.

something that gave her a guilty feeling. She tiptoed out and soon banished the recollection from her thoughts—it was too much to bear. But she soon had pains "in the stomach"; she punished herself and got some forbidden pleasure at the same time. "A chronic indigestion" bothered her until she was twenty, when treatment brought to light the beginnings of her illness.

Here is another life story which shows downward pulls. I have italicized the most significant sentences and phrases.

First this boy was pushed down, then he slid. He is now forty years old. His father, before John was born, *expressed doubts that he would ever amount to anything.* The father, a great *boaster*, had never amounted to anything himself and had lost his own and his wife's money in his business. As soon as the boy was born the father insisted that *he should grow up to be a success in business.* The father then proceeded to *overwhelm* the boy, keeping him on a ranch for six years so that other children would not contaminate him and so that the father's influence would have no rival. As the father was unpredictable in mood, optimistic one day and pessimistic the next, the boy became confused.

"*I want you to do these wonder deeds, but I am afraid you can't,*" the father would tell his son. He never had a word of praise for the boy. In response to the father's rapid-fire manner and overbearing authority the boy became deliberate, reticent, and cowed, and felt inferior to everyone.

At seven he was given sex instruction (sic) by his father, whose face was ashen, whose hands were shaking as he told about the bees and the flowers. His most definite pronouncement was that masturbation led immediately to insanity, which brought mixed emotions to a boy who had masturbated for some years. At eight some sex exploration with three boys led to his being *blackmailed* by a fifteen-year-old, who made him sign a confession. The boy lived in deadly fear. He did not dare leave the house, but peered out of the window as other children played in the yard. During these early years his mother, also overwhelmed by his father,

developed a great capacity for *nagging* at details. Was his hat on
straight, his hair cut right, his face properly washed? Later she
became resentful and began to strike back at her husband,
whether or not the boy was present to see and hear.

His father, meantime, was telling him that he must be a leader.
At boarding school, according to his father's instructions, he
waited for the boys to acknowledge his leadership. He went to
college, and still no one hailed him as a leader. He began to
check up. *Was his father always right?* Was he losing his mind?
He was so occupied by these questions that he gave little time to
studies and was dropped from the school. That gave his mother
the bright idea that he was to go *to the South Sea Islands* and
straighten out his sex life among the natives. He went, and returned with three desires. He wanted to write; his father said
no. He wanted to go to Oxford; his father said no. He wanted to
become a psychiatrist; his father bitterly resented that. And so
he was *sent,* decidedly in the passive voice, to an engineering
school—where he failed.

His father had a sentence for this. *"You are a case of arrested
development, like your mother."*

The family physician referred him to a psychiatrist who won
the boy's confidence and gave him hope. But this was not ac-
complished without interference. The ever-thoughtful father
wrote that "John's thinking about psychiatry would turn any
man's stomach. *He won't be helped by dwelling on the crooked-
ness of minds;* maybe if he would *work on a farm* with supremely
normal folks he would be pulled into self-expression." The
psychiatrist likened this idea to going to the bedside of a typhoid
fever patient and saying, "How would you like to take a three-
day hike in the mountains and get rid of all this sickroom at-
mosphere?"

The boy improved, looked forward to independence, and married. Soon after the marriage the psychiatrist died, and then the
patient's mother. John then became acutely self-conscious, in-
hibited, afraid to walk across open spaces, hopeless. He disguised

much of this by constant *fights with the lawyers* for his mother's estate. He was helped by *retreating into the woods* on camping trips.

By the time he was thirty-six he fought constantly with his wife over the management of their two children. He would spend days *"working out psychological approaches* to better his relationship to his wife," but his wife showed no interest in psychology. He dominated the older boy as his father had dominated him; he wanted the boy to "cooperate"—i.e., to do what he, the father, wanted him to do. Constant rows took place at mealtime. He took to *drink*. Then he went to his office from twelve to two only, and returned home irritable and fatigued. Finally he stopped going to the office altogether *in order to write a book*, and he didn't write the book.

The reader sees that in early life this man was held down and pushed down, so that in later years he drifted—and always downward. The italicized words refer the reader to influences and neuroses which have been mentioned before and will be discussed again, for they are fundamental.

I have been talking about sliding or drifting away from the difficulties that are a part of life—and should be an interesting part. A baseball player becomes bored if he faces a pitcher in practice, with no one to oppose him in the field and no one watching. But if eight more men take the field to prevent him from getting to first base, both he and the onlookers begin to enjoy themselves, even though the batter will be disappointed in his intentions most of the time.

In the mind common to all of us there is, most of the time, something too fearful or too shameful to face. Or else something outside threatens us. We have all sorts of "easy ways out." One of us takes to drink; a second worries about his heart; a third thinks that people on the street are avoiding or snubbing him; a fourth will close his eyes or actually go to sleep; a fifth will blame someone else; a sixth will chatter endlessly.

We use different ways. But it is all the same blind, instinctive flight from fear by letting go or becoming active in another direction. Regardless of future cost, the difficulty, the lion in the path, is not to be faced.

Often for some fine people the thing which is blindly dreaded is actually an aggressive drive, something that should be looked at, sized up, and used. Then the aggression can be neutralized, perhaps by games which either give opportunities to bang into somebody else with satisfaction all around, as in football, or to hit some kind of a ball with some kind of a stick. Better still, the energy behind the aggression can be used in hard work, in town or city, in such activities as slum clearance, which involves tearing down in order to build again.

Here is an example which raises doubts about the good sense of the world in which we live. A college student was tormented in daydreams and dreams at night by visions of overturning and destroying buildings and cities. Within a year or two he was a bombardier over the cities of Germany, carrying out his destructiveness in real life, sanctioned and praised by public opinion. I wish I knew what happened to him after the war. Was his aggression satisfied or increased? And was he destroying to bring about peace—the commonest and perhaps the weakest excuse for war?

Chapter XV

UPLIFT FROM
LOVE AND FAITH

As WITH DOWNWARD PULLS, there are general outside conditions which can pull the individual upward—such things as world peace, adequate housing, democracy, community health, and proper nutrition. But they are beyond the scope of this book, and I turn to those inner forces which help a person to a higher place in the line.

Immediately I run into a difficulty, the same one I met when trying to describe the most normal people. The upward forces do not stand out as vividly as the downward ones. If a bank cashier steals and is arrested it is a subject for many news items, and under his great stress the man is likely to say vivid things. If another cashier retires after forty years of careful and honest handling of other people's money he is not newsworthy, and usually he has nothing to say about what made him honest. Upward influences are generally not front page material because— to the everlasting credit of bank cashiers and most other people —they are the usual and expected motivations.

For this reason I have had to turn to literature more than I did in discussing some of the downward pulls. But patients' voices, and those of close relatives, are still heard.

It is a welcome change to turn to what influences make men advance, climb, move ahead in our line. For evidently there is something in many people which makes them willing to get up on a cold morning and go to work; something that welcomes promotion and new responsibilities. There is a wish to stay well.

The downward pulls were described as being like the drag of gravity—the wish to lie down, to stay in bed. But children delight us because, after they lie down for a while, they begin to crawl, to stand, to walk, jump, and climb. In the long run—and this is the answer—the easy methods fail, and the hard ones can lead to enduring satisfaction.

I say they *can* lead. There is nothing in hardship itself that is constructive. It is hardship endured for a worthy goal that has meaning. There are two accounts of climbing that interest me because one tells of the hard way for its own sake, and the other of a hard struggle for a definite purpose.

The first account, by Longfellow, was mentioned before and is partially excused by its allegorical meaning, but I think its sentimentality and perfectionism are evident. A young man is described as climbing a mountain, carrying a banner emblazoned with a strange device, "Excelsior," which is not good climbing equipment. "The shades of night are falling fast," and a snowstorm is raging as he goes through an Alpine village. There an old man sensibly invites him to rest, but he refuses. A young girl, although she has never met him before, invites him "to stay and rest his weary head upon this breast." But he refuses and staggers on to die in a snowdrift. According to the poem it is wrong to compromise, to wait for daylight and good weather. This youth had a choice which the Scott expedition did not possess. He could have rested, gained strength, and then climbed much farther up his mountain. But the end of a perfectionistic journey is a wasted life.

In a second account, the upward push shines through an article by Rebecca Gross,* in the *Saturday Evening Post* of November 27, 1954. After an automobile accident in which Miss Gross lost one leg just above and the other just below the knee she writes these sentences. "I meet maddening frustrations daily. But nothing is gained by self-pity or retreat from unpleasant

* "I Can Live Without Legs."

reality. . . . Hope has more disciples than despair. The window that lights the darkness of the maimed and handicapped is the instinctive human refusal to give up without a battle. It is good to be able to do things the hard way. The attitude I have taken is realistic—to keep my energies focused. . . . Although I had lost my legs I could still stand on my own feet."

Faced by every inducement a person could have to lie down, to stay in bed, she preferred to stumble and walk and, with the utmost exertion, to climb stairs, not a mountain, in order to go on with her work. She was willing to struggle at the right time and place for a limited result, though she knows that she will always have to face frustrations.

Notice the words that this conquering woman uses, "Nothing is gained by *retreat*"; "the *hard way*" is good; she is *"realistic"*; she is *"focused"*; she *"stands on her own feet"*—even if they aren't there.

She said "yes to life." Echoing that "yes" are the cashiers who keep on being honest; the students who keep on accepting promotion and harder work; the businessmen who accept promotion and increased responsibility; the politicians who after election day face defeat gracefully; the many people who keep their heads in a crisis.

Curiously enough, there are people who blame themselves for the trouble in which they find themselves; others, from scientists to automobile repairmen, who think realistically and control every experiment. There are also people who will take out insurance although it means accepting a present loss for a future gain.

All these people are heading for enduring satisfactions. There is in them a powerful force which makes them act their ages. But partly because they are not apt to break laws, partly because they are not spectacular, they do not force themselves on our attention. A few years ago, however, two of the greatest mile runners were newsworthy because both had overcome severe

leg injuries to develop great leg strength. Many other men and
women have turned an "inferiority complex" into a "golden
opportunity."

The downward ways of flight are fascinating—flight into illness, alcoholism, daydreams, geography, death. But the heroic
men of the Scott expedition to the South Pole decided to meet
death head on by marching on when they knew there was no
hope. Jacqueline Cochran, too, met fear head on when she was
a child. Going by a "haunted cemetery" in the dark she saw a
ghost in her path; she ran ahead to grapple with it and found
that it was a calf. This frontal attack on fear became a guiding
force in her adventurous life.

Although the people of our line are adults, it is necessary to
look backward into childhood and adolescence, even to infancy,
to find what has prepared men and women to advance instead
of retreat.

My own phrase for the most powerful constructive force in
youth has been "love and a plan." Love and full protection for
the baby are followed by love and no protection for the grownup,
with many gradual steps in between. Love which does not change
as the amount of dependence changes. Love which unselfishly
lets children grow into their own lives in their own ways to become credits to themselves in a new family and a changing world.

A "plan" demands much from the parents. It is the opposite
of "anything to keep Tommy quiet for the moment." It means
seldom doing for a child what the child has learned to do by
himself. It means never being surprised or hurt when a boy or
girl at fifteen or sixteen acts like a boy or a girl of fifteen or sixteen.

Love with a plan is not easy, but it brings the richest rewards
that a parent can know. Perhaps "plan" is too strong a word.
"Unselfish love" covers the whole idea. Some parents, without
thinking much about it, meet the growth of their children
naturally and easily. They lift them, but they do not push them.

We are not talking of erotic love. Maternal love is nearer the mark, and "loving care" is close. But floundering about for terms and definitions seems superfluous when we read the New Testament, and especially, "Thou shalt love thy neighbor as thyself." The use of the word "charity" in the King James version suggests the meaning we seek. "Charity envieth not; . . . is not puffed up, . . . seeketh not her own, is not easily provoked. . . . And now abideth faith, hope, charity, these three; but the greatest of these *is* charity." * This implies love with compassion and respect.

Even in a modern dictionary the first meaning of charity is Christian love, the second is good will, and only the third is liberality to the poor. But nowadays the third meaning has crowded out the other two.

This love that favors growth can be given by a teacher. Two superior college graduates, brought up in the slums of New York, told me that their lives were turned toward success and happiness by two teachers whom they met in consecutive grades in crowded schools. Theodore Dreiser describes such a teacher: "This girl, . . . who really did teach me in the best sense of the word, spelled opportunity instead of repression. . . . At once, and for some reason, she seemed to take an interest in me. . . . I was so moved by this consideration that I was silent, and yet tremulous with pleasure. . . . She said, 'Theodore, you read beautifully.' . . . I was very proud. . . . Some scenes . . . and some thoughts and emotions have a deathless quality of their own." †

To give point to loving words from teachers, let me instance words of hatred which also had "a deathless quality of their own." A friend of mine, a distinguished surgeon, told me of making a foolish mistake in his first Latin class, a mistake forgivable in a sensitive boy of thirteen. Never in four years did the Latin teacher let him forget it, but made him the butt of the

---

* I Cor. 13:4, 5, 13.

† Theodore Dreiser, *Dawn.* Liveright Publishing Corp., New York, 1931, pp. 192 and 194. By permission of World Publishing Co., Cleveland, Ohio, publisher of this title since 1934.

class, pouring ridicule and sarcasm upon him. At seventeen, on leaving school, my friend was honestly convinced that he was stupid and of little account. Later, in medical school (admission was easier in those days), he began to notice that he did things as well as the next man, and at the end of internship and residencies he had confidence in himself as a surgeon. But in his seventy-fifth year he refused to speak to the daughter of the Latin teacher and would go out of his way to avoid her. Thirteen to seventy-five is a fairly long time to bear a grudge!

We can easily see that religion may also be a mighty force for uplift. Religion which exalts love, favors growth, builds a constructive and affirmative conscience and regards distant goals can greatly improve the mental health of the individual and of society. It can rescue a man from the downward drift, turning him the other way. This it can do in its own field and in its own right.

The medicine we have today is not that of 1855 or 1755, of the Dark Ages or of Roman, Greek, or Biblical times. It is highly differentiated. Yet some clergymen are reported to have claimed that, in healing services conducted by their churches, cancer, paralysis, and locomotor ataxia have been cured. Imagine such a clergyman, without any engineering training, claiming that he could build a suspension bridge over the Hudson at New York City!

In the Council for Clinical Training of Theological Students there were some general conclusions to which the students and their instructors came. They agreed that faith is an upward pull in illness as it is in health. A physician from Amsterdam put the same idea into these words: "Every year I take a trainload of patients to the shrine at Lourdes. My hardheaded Dutchmen do not find miracles, but they return to recover more quickly, to suffer more patiently, to die more nobly."

Faith is an upward pull in sickness and in health, in war and in peace. "Religion and psychiatry should cooperate and not compete in the field of mental health" is the judgment of the

Rev. James Van DerVeldt, professor of psychology at the Catholic University, Washington, D.C. "Psychiatry is no substitute for religion: religion is no substitute for psychiatry." In "a serious mental breakdown," a person "may—if he so wishes—go to church and light a candle, but right after that it would be a sensible thing for him to visit the office of a psychiatrist." *

Normal anxiety belongs in the religious field. Given the present state of the world, the person without anxiety must be stupid or deluded. Being a person, a self, in a great population, facing dangers and death from other people and from the catastrophes which nature may bring, is a proper cause for normal anxiety. The kind of religion which gives constructive values and courageous faith helps combat this realistic anxiety.

But neurotic anxiety is in the psychiatric field. Here is inner conflict, its sources unknown, a mental uneasiness looking for some spot on which to land. Relief may come from a landing place on or in the body which seems external to the mind. No matter what form the neurotic anxiety takes, it means that the individual carries a load which seems "unbearable."

Please recall that in *Lady in the Dark*, the restless anxiety of a woman of forty was shown to have come "from the exquisite forgotten agony of a child of four." It had been forgotten, and it was the psychiatrist's task to bring into the main stream of thought the buried cause of her neurotic anxiety. So the psychiatrist's dark province lies largely below the point where religious healing and uplift begin, though he may humbly acknowledge that he gets help from secret forces which operate more deeply within the human mind. What they are and whence they come he does not presume to say.

* By permission from *Psychiatry and Catholicism*, 2nd edition, by Van DerVeldt and Odenwald. Copyright, 1957. McGraw-Hill Book Co., New York.

Chapter XVI

IN DEFENSE
OF PSYCHIATRISTS

As SECRETARY for some years to the American Psychiatric Association and always a member of a staff of a large hospital, I have known many psychiatrists very well. Using the word "good" to mean—as it usually does—decent, honest, and capable, I recognize that psychiatrists are good, bad, or indifferent. As a group they are about as normal as most people; they compare well with clergymen and bankers and labor leaders. They are distinguished by an intense devotion—sometimes even a neurotic one—to their patients, and this is often accompanied by a lack of attention to their own families. But this is a state of mind shared by other physicians, by reformers, by people who aim at leadership in business and elsewhere.

Testimony by psychiatrists in court cases which are sensational enough to get into the newspapers seems to make an unfavorable impression on the public. A glance at our line shows one reason. Physicians accustomed to seeing normality in terms of 10 per cent to 90 per cent try to talk with lawyers used to thinking of sanity as 100 per cent or zero. Both sides are right; it is the mixture that is wrong. Both lawyers and psychiatrists are trying to remedy a poor situation.

The following three stories illustrate an occupational hazard which is shared by almost all practitioners of medicine.

From one tragic situation I escaped self-blame and criticism from other people through no virtue of my own but through the timing of a suicide. A young woman I had never seen, but whose mother I knew, telephoned one noon to ask if she could come in to see me. At that time I was medical director of a hospital and had no timed appointments for the afternoon, so I told her to come along. She said, "You are kind; I'll come in and weep on your shoulder." She started to drive in, but in a small woodland she killed herself with motor fumes.

I have often wondered how guilty I would have felt if I had been facing an afternoon filled with appointments with patients whom I did not feel it right to disappoint. It would have been natural to say, "Come tomorrow or next week." But there is another aspect to this which is connected with the next illustration. Suppose the young woman had come to my office, been partly reassured by the interview, been clear and calm, and then had committed suicide on the way home. I can hear a malicious chorus: "This young woman took her troubles to a psychiatrist and *then* killed herself."

A psychiatrist just beginning practice has borne the brunt of exactly this malice. A young man in the university, whose severe problems were known to a group of medical students, came to this physician as the academic year closed and made appointments for treatment to begin in the fall. The student went home to New York and ran into an unexpected and disastrous situation which aggravated his illness and resulted in his suicide. In this case members of his family, who knew nothing of the student's predicament, said that this "normal boy went to see Dr. ———, a psychiatrist, and was so upset by the interview that he killed himself." The young doctor cannot defend himself because he cannot divulge his patient's secret. As well blame the Weather Bureau for the hurricanes that sweep over us!

In another instance blame was attached to psychoanalysts in Vienna and Berlin by the mother of a boy who was to enter college in the fall. The mother's attitude can be judged by the fact that she expected to go to college with him and share his room. The boy, with desperate insight, saved some money in the summer and ran to Europe, where he saw two distinguished analysts. He was received with understanding and sympathy, and as he had made no arrangements for remaining abroad and still intended to enter college, they advised him to consult an American psychiatrist. On the voyage home the boy became confused and violent and has never improved. The mother, never thinking of her own eighteen years of influence on her son, keeps saying, "Just see, it took those analysts only two hours to upset my boy!" Here the mother was the tornado and the analysts the Weather Bureau.

It has always helped me to remember what my teacher, Dr. Shattuck, said to our medical school class. "Gentlemen, you will be blamed many times for things that were not your fault, but think of the times you will get credit for recoveries which were not your fault, either."

In the February 25, 1956, issue of the *Saturday Evening Post* the first article is a criticism of psychiatrists. It is entitled "Who Cares About Us?" and it is curious that the author answers the question herself. The nearest state hospital and its social worker do care, she says, but nobody else. "Through it I have found the sort of help I have needed all these years." But before the author found this nearby help she had to struggle desperately with wild excitements in her husband. She and the patient drove from California to Boston to see a psychiatrist, whose time was fully booked for weeks ahead. Under pressure, this physician saw the patient, who made a good impression under the influence of phenobarbital, and the doctor dismissed the man to take the long trip over again.

The author of the article suggests that every psychiatrist should employ a social worker to give attention to the family. The suggestion is a good one, but while there are too few psychiatrists, there are even fewer psychiatric social workers. It is the old story: "not enough of anyone or anything except patients." Every excitement causes exquisite suffering to some family member, but why should a physician in Boston take time from his Massa-

chusetts patients to treat a man from California whose illness
was not evident in a short interview?

A cluster of misunderstandings stands between the public and
psychiatrists.

One of the most important is the natural resentment against
the idea that another person can know why you behave as you
do, better than you know yourself, and that that other person
must therefore feel superior. Some of this resentment disappears
if you consider that a psychiatrist takes for granted that he is
subject to the same general up and down pulls that influence
his patient, and that he is trying to help his patient to recognize
and deal with these pulls. And there is an inner core—"in the
middle of my middle there's a middle that is I"—which the
psychiatrist does not want or need to touch. His professional
job is rather to clear away obstacles to the freedom of that
"inner I." Instead of feeling himself holier, a good psychiatrist
is constantly amazed at his likeness to his patient.

In the *Atlantic Monthly* of January, 1949, appeared a poem
by R. P. Lister which is beautiful in itself and also contains lines
applicable to conscience and to other important human conditions. First I changed its subject, quoted a few separate lines,
and added a last line of my own. Then, with the author's consent, I cite this unusual and thought-provoking poem in its
entirety.

My conscience is "an onion, you may peel it if you will. . . .
In the middle of my middle lies another middle still.
There is nothing in the middle, say the wise ones, and they lie."
In the middle of my middle, there's a middle that is I.

And now the original, *My Heart Is Like an Onion*, by R. P.
Lister.

My HEART is like an onion, you may peel it if you will,
But you will not find a kernal like a protoplasmic pill;
In the middle of my middle lies another middle still.

Many layers has that onion; I have peeled them one by one
From the fading of the planets to the setting of the sun,
But the task was so enormous that it hardly was begun.

You could peel it for a fortnight, you could peel it for a year,
But the end that you were seeking would still be nowhere near,
Though you peeled in utter frenzy, crying madly, Is it here?

There is nothing in the middle, say the wise ones, with a sigh;
There is nothing in the middle, say the wise ones, and they lie.
There are forty million middles, and every one is I.

And some of them are virtuous, and some of them are ill,
And every tiny layer—you may peel them if you will—
Conceals another layer that is even smaller still.

Another mistaken idea is that the psychiatrist is a person looking for trouble, although it is true that hunting for symptoms is
a large part of the education and practice of all physicians and
surgeons. But soon every doctor begins to see health when patients and their families see disease. Cardiologists spend perhaps
half of their time assuring would-be patients that their hearts
are working well. Psychiatrists are continually discovering that
what seems abnormal behavior is really normal reaction to abnormal surroundings.

Very few people in the community recognize that, contrary
to popular opinion, in every large hospital for mental diseases a
continuing struggle is going on between the psychiatrists want-
ing to push patients out and families who want to keep those
patients in. The psychiatrists see the normal; the families remember the abnormal.

Now to go back to some of the misunderstandings about psychoanalysis.

Fathers and mothers, husbands and wives of patients in
analysis, are in an uncomfortable spot. They want to help, and
are told that the analyst wants no help. They want to know how

much longer the treatment will continue, and are told that no one can tell. They feel that the patient is more wrapped up in and more devoted to the analyst than he is to them, and they are told to stay out of the picture. Somehow or other, through a third person, they should also be told that psychoanalysis is an intimate relationship between analyst and patient and that involvement of a third person muddies the waters and lengthens the treatment. And many successful analyses have taken only four years, the length of a college education, which is not too high a price in time to pay for bringing one's mind up to date.

Here is an example of the completely unjust accusations that are made against analysts.

A husband and wife consulted me after they had agreed on a divorce. They told me their situation was unbearable. The wife, realizing that part of the trouble was a neurosis in the husband, agreed to postpone action until after he had had an analysis. This disclosed a war tragedy which happened long before the marriage; it helped the husband to an emotional balance which he had not possessed before, but it did not change his attitude or his wife's about the divorce. Many friends of the couple said, "See, the analysis caused the separation." In fact, the analysis had nothing whatever to do with the divorce except to delay it.

Many unfair comments on analysis are illustrated by the joke, "They analyzed her for months, and she was running around with everyone else's husband, and then they found it was only her tonsils." It is not too funny as a joke. In my own experience a boy of nineteen who was living in an unreal world of alcoholism, gangsters, dope adventures, and delusions of grandeur was operated on by a surgeon who held up an infected appendix and said, "This is the cause of all John's troubles. Don't mess around with psychiatrists." A month later, and twenty years later, John was still living in the same unreal world, but in a state hospital.

What is wrongly called "common sense" demands a quick removal of something to cure the mental patient. Take out his tonsils, his teeth, his appendix! Take out the wrong idea that

makes him irrational or difficult! "Just get at the trouble and cut
it out." Physicians and psychiatrists fervently wish that it was
as simple as that.

I have always been grateful to Peggy Bacon, writing in the
New Yorker, for verses which give dignity and beauty to psychoanalysis and describe an unconscious mind in all of us:

> Those old events are sunken ships,
> That happiness a fluted shell;
> Around them tidal memory slips
> Her undulating spell.

> The derelicts of all our past
> The bodies of our life are drowned,
> Vibrating gently, anchored fast,
> Uneasy for a sound.*

I close my defense with an example of psychiatry at its best,
taken from a letter to a hospital about a former patient.

A man with many relatives who were mentally unstable had
been a brilliant, critical, egotistic, idealistic youth. At thirty-four
and forty-five he had delusions of persecution and looked to
Hitler and Stalin to save the human race; he was in turn Judas
and the Devil. In the hospital where I was working he was dis-
tractible, full of fear and panic when he talked about the symbolic
meanings of what he saw and heard. The hospital surroundings
helped him; he saw in them a protection, and he was cooperative
and slowly developed insight. When the physicians at the hospital sent him home they recommended continued psychotherapy
near his home. The family found in the psychiatrist of a nearby
sanitarium a man "who had the power and the charm to release
in James his creative, productive talents and to lead him to maturity." All has gone well for five years.

The letter giving this information closes with these words
about a colleague of mine, to my knowledge a very busy man.

* Peggy Bacon, "Remembrance of Youth" (third and fifth stanzas), November 20, 1943. © 1943 The New Yorker Magazine, Inc.

"I shall never forget all we owe to Dr. S. of appreciation and gratitude. I think of him as an unfailing outstretched hand, always there to turn to through many, many years."

Psychiatrists are really human beings with different characters, abilities, and weaknesses. Most of them want to help people to reach their own inner, untrammeled selves and come to a true integrity.

Chapter XVII

UPWARD PULLS
FROM PSYCHIATRY

IN ADDITION to the upward pulls which men and women have used instinctively, there are others which have been influenced by suggestions from psychiatry. I have no wish to go into the treatment of mental diseases or the complicated research activities which bring hope for more and more recoveries in the near future. But from such treatment and from such research come suggestions that are clear and simple and applicable to many of the problems of everyday life.

Analysts and psychotherapists have developed as their powerful but somewhat tricky tool the intricate hour-long interview which can be used by a few highly trained people. From this complex device have come ideas about better methods of listening—the art of listening in family and business life.

It is decidedly a modern idea that parents should listen to their children, teachers to their pupils, clergymen to their parishioners. Such listening, thoughtfully managed, can be a potent remedy for misunderstanding and can prevent unnecessary friction. One great difficulty is inherent—it takes time; and the time element enters into and modifies every listening procedure.

Simplicity and power are in this illustration. After the death of Dr. Daniel Fuller, an Italian mother came to tell me this story in her halting English. She had been deeply troubled by the behavior of her son, who had had an inflammation of the brain. She said, "That important man, Dr. Fuller, let me talk to him all I wanted for an hour and a half; he was sympathetic, and I told him a lot. You know, it was the only time in my life that a man has listened to me for over five minutes. I shall never stop praying for him." Notice that the time was an hour and a half and also that the same help, in the same way, could have been given by a clergyman, an employer, or a teacher.

A professor of psychology, Dr. Norman Maier, relates this interview between a listening employer and a disgruntled employee in his *Principles of Human Relations: Applications to Management.** A Miss Everett complained that she never got an increase in pay when the pay of other clerks was advanced. She then raised several criticisms calculated to make the employer angry; he responded by saying, "I see," even when she said, "If I were pretty you'd give me an increase" and "You don't want me here." She wept; the manager passed out Kleenex and waited. Then Miss Everett began to tell how her father's death seemed to have started her unhappiness and how she was in good shape financially. For half an hour they exchanged ideas about travel. Then Miss Everett suggested that it would help if she lived with another girl and made other interests for herself. She left in a friendly manner, but after two hours; she had found a listener, and her grievance was gone.

I emphasize the time factor, which enhances the values listening can bring, and I offer some tragic examples to show what lack of time can do in the medical field, although the examples must be fully as frequent in the field of business.

A man fell and fractured his left collarbone. Because the surgeon knew that in many similar cases an unsightly callus had formed, he used extreme immobilization of the arm. The patient made a good recovery, but then threw himself into the river because his livelihood and his chief interest in life lay in playing the violin. The treatment had stiffened his wrist and fingers so that he could no longer play well. Attention to a part destroyed the whole. Lack of time to find out about the whole personality destroyed the careful surgery and long aftercare.

* Reprinted with permission. John Wiley & Sons, Inc., New York, 1952.

A woman engaged expensive and time-consuming attention in a dozen hospitals in New York and Philadelphia during seven years. Laboratory examinations and medical and surgical care continued over months. Finally it was found that by ingenious methods she had been able to produce hemorrhages all over her body. If, when she first applied for help, a social worker could have had an hour's interview with her, she could easily have discovered that when this woman was well her husband beat her and when she was sick she found sympathy from the hospital doctors and nurses.

In another case two psychiatrists, each giving over an hour to a patient, were able to make severe surgical operations unnecessary by being good listeners. In one instance dizziness and deafness, in another a dangerously rising basal metabolism disappeared as the patients poured out their resentments and fears.

From long experience and by common consent psychiatrists have established the hour-long interview as their time unit for active therapy. This time unit, along with some other suggestions, they recommend to listeners everywhere—to parents and employers especially.

An important suggestion is to use silence, and a simple illustration is what a mother said to me, every one of her remarks being followed by a pause and silence on my part. "I must be strict with my children. ——— I slapped Betsy extra hard yesterday because she irritated me—was I wrong? ——— It was because I was mad at my husband. ——— Yes, I was wrong and I'm sorry." This was her own conclusion, and I had offered nothing to distract her from it.

Another suggestion is that the listener use no word or other intimation of praise or blame, at least until the story is completely told. However, minor questions about times and places to get the story straight need not interrupt and are allowable.

Through a few words and long silences an attitude of the listener can be made known. It implies, "I have such respect for you as you meet a difficult situation that I expect you to come to your own solution."

And finally, if the listener has problems of his own—and who doesn't?—those should be kept completely out of the interview. One person's troubles are complicated enough; put another set of troubles in with them and you have a merry-go-round. For the purpose of the interview the listener, no matter how troubled at other times, must be steady and completely—not partially—interested in the other person. For a while he must be altogether unselfish.

There are certain positions in life that traditionally are censorious, corrective, critical, preaching; there are judges, teachers, clergy, parents. These persons should learn the art of listening, which has helped many to go upward on the long line.

There are other notions for our ordinary living which come from the study of tangled loves and hates which is psychiatry. This is because neurosis and delusion are like prejudice, which is perhaps the greatest evil in the world. Dr. Douglas Bond says, "The essence of the neurotic process, which is more or less in everyone, is prejudice or the displacement of emotion from where it rightfully belongs to a new object—a person, a thing, an idea, a part of the body." In other words, behind the neurosis, delusion, or prejudice we must look for the *emotion*, not the *reason*.

You can't argue prejudice away. But, like neurosis, it is possible to manage it as if it were a conditioned reflex. Bring the object of prejudice into view at some distance under unexciting circumstances; then bring it closer and closer, and the original emotion may die out. A Southern professor, joining a faculty one of whose members was a Negro, at first kept as far away from him at the faculty lunch table as was possible; then he sat anywhere and, finally, he came in eagerly talking with his former aversion, sitting down beside him to finish the discussion.

In general, prejudice tends to disappear with wide travel,

stepping over local boundaries. The very natural clinging to the familiar is the essential ingredient of much prejudice and distrust, and fear of strangers can disappear if one lives with and gets to know them. Clinging to the home base is characteristic of neurosis.

While argument is of no use, facts are a different thing. The articles and pictures about men and women of our minorities and of other nations, spread on the pages of our national magazines, are effective because they are not arguments but news, facts which cannot be disputed.

It seems to me—and I may be mistaken—that two items about Dr. Ralph Bunche had different effects upon people prejudiced against the Negro. An account of his conducting negotiations between warring nations, as a distinguished American, was powerful because it could not be twisted, and Dr. Bunche stood out as an individual. But a second item of news, coming later, was of Dr. Bunche's refusing a State Department post because he did not at that time want to live in Washington under its segregation rules. Here the issue was soon confused by proponents of segregation as they dropped Dr. Bunche from the discussion and talked first of all the colored population of Washington, then of the poorest part of it, and finally of the criminal part. Dr. Bunche in the Near East stood out as an individual of dignity and worth; in Washington there was an attempt to lose him in the crowd. The criminal population of the city, colored or white, had nothing to do with Dr. Bunche or his decision of some years ago.

In Philadelphia an experiment has been going on to explain religious rites to small mixed groups of five- and six-year-olds. A Jewish mother described the Jewish holiday of Hanukkah; a Catholic nun explained the details of her costume and the rosary. Plenty of prejudice had been formed in the minds of children at these early ages! The children had "learned what they lived"— what was in the air around them. A look at the school textbooks showed that these pictured white people, mostly with Anglo-Saxon names, in comfortable houses. But again the national magazines gave a truer picture—of college football teams with names from all corners of the earth, of the slums of our cities, of contrasts in skin color.

Participating in a common purpose has removed prejudice, especially in a common emergency or danger. In Korea a correspondent described the return of a patrol of eight men from a reconnaissance where each man's life had been dependent on the seven others. Two were South Koreans, four were white, and two were Negro soldiers. Prejudice cannot survive in such a situation.

A Philadelphia physician I know is active in working with the National Association of Physical and Recreational Instructors because he believes that in games there is an ideal dissolver of prejudice. A real opposite to prejudice is good sportsmanship. Over fifty years ago a colored boy was quarterback on a team from a preparatory school which sent most of its players into college teams. Playing against some of his former teammates, this quarterback found that he was being especially roughed and sat upon. To an old friend on the opposing team he said, "You used to say that you would never treat a colored boy different from a white one." The other man said, "Oh, we are not ganging up on you because you are colored, but because you are the best player on your team." Certainly in athletics Negroes are breaking through, after bitter times, our own Iron Curtain.

But the greatest weapon against prejudice is to recognize the individual in any group. Mr. Crothers put it: "We see only groups and pride ourselves on our own defective vision. A finer gift is the ability to know a man when we see one. Our proper task is to deal justly with each single life." *

We tend to think that members of a group can be judged together. But line up any group for a hundred-yard dash, or a mile

* Samuel M. Crothers, *The Pardoner's Wallet.* Houghton Mifflin Co., Boston, 1905, p. 80.

run, and one man will come in first and one last and the rest in
between. I wish that people could use a chant something like
this for all groups over a thousand:

> Anglo-Saxons are good, bad, and indifferent.
> Catholics are good, bad, and indifferent.
> Lawyers are good, bad, and indifferent.
> Negroes are good, bad, and indifferent.
> Republicans are good, bad, and indifferent.
> Presbyterians are good, bad, and indifferent.

Every large group has in it talented, dull, hard-working, lazy,
virtuous, and criminal members.

A school boy was asked, "Who was the first man?" and replied,
"George Washington." When told it was Adam, he said "Well,
if you want to count foreigners!"

Those who uphold the worth of the individual are in good
company. They line up for world peace instead of isolationism,
democracy instead of totalitarianism, for the individual student
or patient instead of the stereotyping and overcrowding in schools
and hospitals. They line up with love against the myriad forms of
hate which are the components of the prejudices that hurt.

To look into the boast of "free, white, and twenty-one" is to
find prejudice, ignorance, and wishful thinking. You see the
wish to be one of a favored race and the childish idea that one
automatically becomes adult at twenty-one, a magical age which
brings full maturity! And as twenty-one may indeed be free, just
as often it may be bound by a thousand invisible threads which
keep one from making a present decision on appropriate grounds.
Free, or bound by the tyranny of the past with its fears, mistaken
attitudes, habits? "Oh, to find oneself becoming a free human
being at sixty-two."

The remedies for prejudice lie in encouraging people to accept new ideas, to enter new mental combinations, to have open
minds, to let in truth even when it hurts; to expect that reasonableness and realism will some day focus as much on the rela-

tionships between human beings as they now do on atomic research.

"I don't like her and I'll find a reason yet." This is *Punch's* summary of the present situation.

A third upward pull comes from psychiatry to general medicine. The power of emotion, which stands out so clearly in psychiatric practice, is being recognized by general practitioners, who have certain advantages over psychiatrists and certain disadvantages.

The family physician can meet emotional upsets soon after they begin, and his relationship to the patient is already established. The younger the ailment the sooner it can be cured; if it is five minutes old it should be stopped in five minutes; if a week old it should take a week; if five or more years old it may take five years.

A medical student, after hearing a vivid lecture on heart disease, became alarmed about his own heart. Luckily he was able to find his family doctor, who examined him thoroughly and then complimented him on his fine state of health. And thus a beginning cardiac neurosis was allayed.

One medical specialist caused a neurosis on Monday which was cured by another specialist on Tuesday. The first man told a woman that she had a heart murmur and a blood pressure five points above normal, and prescribed digitalis. The second, a cardiologist and a man who knew the intimate connection of emotion and the heart, completely reassured the patient by telling her casually that both the slight increase in pressure and the murmur were helpful responses, and by taking away the digitalis.

Of late the *Journal of the American Medical Association* in its articles and editorials has been suggesting to all clinical physicians and surgeons that they avoid creating symptoms by remembering that their patients are usually anxious persons, ready with their families to misinterpret and exaggerate. So it advises the doctor not to show anxiety in his facial expression, not to discuss or dictate symptoms in the patient's presence, and not to seek too long for a physical cause when there may be an emotional one.

The introduction of emotional factors into every diagnosis would tremendously complicate the growing intricacies of medicine if it were not for common sense. If the symptoms of a new patient fall into line and meet the textbook requirements, the doctor can then go ahead with only a passing interest in emotional factors. If, however, the symptoms are not in line, or fluctuate, then he should give physical and emotional factors an even chance.

But if the family doctor and also the pediatrician have the advantage of being first on the scene with their relationship established, they also meet that tremendous obstacle to the study of the emotions which we have discussed earlier—lack of time to listen. The psychiatrist has his hour-long interviews, but he sees only a few patients a day. The family physician must see many more, and usually his only recourse is to listen for a few minutes at a time over many visits; if he listens for a long time to one patient it will be at the expense of others. The pediatrician probably sees the most patients, as he has to deal with all the modern immunizations.

The fact is that for good and sufficient reasons doctors cannot find the time to do enough listening. Sometimes they can get nurses or social workers to listen for them. But it is comforting to know that doctors in general are more and more conscious of the effect of emotions and the need to prevent unnecessary fears. Most doctors are beginning to appreciate what listening to anyone for many hours can do to stop all sorts of physical illnesses which are unnecessarily taking up much precious time. Let me close with an example.

In psychiatry the most complex process is an analysis, a proceeding requiring an hour a day about five times a week over two or three years. A verbatim account of such an analysis would be a most boring thing to read. But once in a while an able writer is able to condense his or her experience and give it to us in a readable book.

In *Fight against Fears*,* Lucy Freeman describes the constant physical ailments that beset her before she was analyzed. Added to her colds and cramps and aches was the fear of death, cancer, and snubs which is shared by many thousands of sensitive people. She dressed badly.

During analysis, she was helped by the physician's emphasis on a love which served and did not expect to be served.

After the analysis the physical troubles completely disappeared, she became easy in mind, dressed well, "liked herself," and was not discouraged when she was not perfect.

Out of this condensation of a process which seems devious, almost out of this world, come some simple suggestions for every life. One of them is that physical illnesses, overactivity, a tendency to punish oneself, can come from things not appropriate to one's present position but from things long forgotten which really should have nothing to do with the case. The analysis shows that "dressing badly" can be a deep refusal to respect oneself; that a demand for perfection can be vainglorious; that imperfections can be unimportant matters to be forgotten in a large enterprise; that, for example, stuttering is not important if one says the right thing.

Every analysis, every deep and complicated study of an inner life, invites and puts an obligation upon the psychiatrist, who plays a small part in this world, to place the simple things he learns at the disposal of the most normal and gifted people he can find.

* Crown Publishers, Inc., New York, 1951.

Chapter XVIII

UPWARD PULLS
FROM THE HOSPITAL

TREASURE UPON TREASURE and lesson upon lesson for all of us lie ready to be revealed in every psychiatric hospital. They are deeply buried when there are too many patients and too few therapists and investigators. Most of them must wait until communities, legislatures, and private benefactors provide the opportunity to discover and make use of them. Some are brought to light by devoted men and women who struggle against red tape and lack of time and money to find the individual human being among the multitudes under their care.

There are special reasons for the study of hospital patients. Under controlled observation they show in exaggeration the faults and the virtues of all the rest of us; they write large for us to see plainly. "They are just like ourselves only more so" is worth repeating. They are split apart along natural lines of cleavage so that we can see into them. They are honest in expressing thoughts and feelings.

Let me mention some of the advantages of life in a mental hospital. A recovered patient, Olivia Harlan, writes in an *Atlantic Monthly* article * about private hospitals, which she logically but mistakenly prefers to call asylums in the old and good meaning of places of refuge.

"In all but one of the asylums in which I have been there has prevailed a *tolerance* for all human idiosyncrasies. More was forgiven and gladly forgotten than anywhere else I have been.

* "Minds in the Mending," September, 1941, p. 330.

184

. . . Uninhibited pranks and frankly bawdy remarks are never alluded to after a patient has been promoted."

Who are the patients? "Dull individuals do not as a rule crack up mentally or emotionally. . . . It is the artist, the idealist, the childlike person of great faith whose belief has been betrayed. . . . I had grown immeasurably in the hospital year, but my friends, when I returned to them, the young married crowd of successful, happy, pleasantly well-to-do, average intellectual persons, suddenly seemed like a group of backward and badly spoiled children whose only conversation consisted of the most tiresome inanities. A remark I made the other day that most of my best friends were in or had just left asylums was greeted with shouts of wildest mirth."

The lessons to be drawn from this hospital experience are plain enough. We greatly need more tolerance in family and social life. It might be well for many people to take a course in a sanitarium and learn to know and put up with interesting, irregular people. Where can be found more original ideas, less slavery to convention, more truth, and less false politeness? After such a stay a person could return to everyday life and its restrictions with a new understanding of the uses and abuses of convention and of the danger inherent in all unmitigated virtues.

In addition to tolerance, a hospital offers promotion after protection. A Mrs. B. had recovered from an attack of depression in a psychiatric department. Seven years later she again became depressed and with two nurses began a seven-hour ride to Philadelphia. On the long ride she made desperate attempts to commit suicide. Arriving at the hospital gate she suddenly relaxed and said, "Now it is up to the hospital—I'm out of it." For a time all responsibility was taken away from her; the last thing she wanted was "an open door." Then she was promoted— responsibilities given back to her as she showed strength to meet them—to the convalescent ward and then to her home.

Patients in a mental hospital can talk and act free from the feeling that what they say reverberates and affects those they love or hate at home. As they talk to trained listeners they hurt no one, and what they say is used to help them at the time and is kept in notes to help others in the future.

Great lessons sometimes come from hospital patients for whom there is little hope. Such patients were quoted in Chapter III where Mary Tree taught what can happen when burning desire is walled in by circumstance. Also in that chapter a young man explained the family events which can turn a quiet and gentlemanly little boy into a killer. And Angela showed what is the only continuing abode for a person who builds all her life on daydreams. For all three the hospital was the only fitting place, but from all three comes the demonstration of the need for unselfish love in the formation of character everywhere.

Other things are taught by hospital patients who get well. In the most severe swings of mood one sees plainly that a strong emotion sweeps reason out of its way, makes its own decisions, and then tries to justify itself by false reasoning. Nothing in everyday life stands out so clearly, and nothing is more important in that everyday life. Emotion sometimes can make decisions that are superior to those made by reason. When that is so it is well to acknowledge it. These sentences should end with a full stop, a period: "I love her." "I love my son." They should not be spoiled by trailing rationalizations: "I love my son because. . . ."

Then there are patients who have apparently gone downhill for years in hospital life until they seem "deteriorated, demented, hopeless," but have suddenly come back to full and creative mental health. Right here is a message of hope to the men on Skid Row, the women in alcoholism, the long-time losers everywhere. Not only hospitals but other retreats can serve as stopping places, neutral zones, where down-and-outers can "lie down to bleed awhile and then get up to fight again."

Ethel Mason was not wanted by her mother, who had made a hasty elopement, or by her father, who soon divorced her mother. When the mother married again the stepfather was

cold and unfair to the child. When Ethel was six her mother
was divorced a second time. At the age of ten Ethel was sexually
involved with a number of boys; at fourteen she entered vacant
houses with a gang of girls and explored homosexuality; at sixteen she ran away from school. Her real father remarried, and
Ethel was sure that she wasn't wanted. She stole $3.00 and tried
to get a gun to rob a gas station. At seventeen she was sent to a
school for the feebleminded and was there kept in confinement
for a week.

By this time she had been given the following diagnoses:
sexual delinquent, criminal, feebleminded, psychopath, schizophrenic. She was sent to a hospital for mental diseases, and
there she met doctors and nurses who accepted her as a person
in her own right and who saw her covered-up good qualities. In
a brief summer she lost her depression and pessimism and
suicidal thoughts. She eventually went to college and while there
was elected secretary of her class; then to work as a secretary.
She decided on psychoanalysis, which she paid for herself, and
she made a happy marriage. Now she is conscientious, full of
sympathy for the underdog, and in all respects a good and useful
person.

Ella Holmes at twenty was tied to a job which she despised—
a monotonous "easy" job which a ten-year-old could have done.
She broke down with very serious symptoms. She was "ice or
stone," she turned other people into "ice," and so she came to
a psychiatric hospital and remained six months. As she recovered she was filled with new ambition, went to college, and became chief dietitian in a great general hospital. The mental
hospital had opened a door.

After a hospital treatment by insulin shock a young woman
had words to say that are illuminating. "It was in a discarded
newspaper that I read about insulin treatments. Arrangements
were made for me to come to the Pennsylvania Hospital and I
came." At this time "I wanted to talk like a baby; to live like a
responsible adult caused physical pain. The different parts of my

body seemed disconnected." After the insulin treatment, "I went out for a ride, and it seemed a veil had been taken away from my eyes and brain. The earth looked fair. . . . I felt myself once more a part of the world and able to enjoy it."

The hospital environment can be a constructive retreat from the entanglements of family. A patient can talk and act out his troubles without affecting and involving the people for whom he has responsibility. As Dr. William A. White used to say, "Where can a man be crazy except in a mental hospital?" where he does no damage by being irresponsible.

Certainly the hospitals would yield their treasures—not only for their patients but for the world outside—if their possibilities could be recognized. They could develop ties to the communities about them that would keep up general interest in mental health. They could become centers for education in character building, forums in which citizens, clergy, businessmen, and psychiatrists could study and argue the bases of man's predicament. The patients would provide searching comments on the manners and customs of us all.

The reason that most large hospitals do not fill this role is that the communities and the legislatures think of mental patients as a race apart. "We do not have anything in common with them." Here is the value of the line. If every citizen had his own line in mind, with himself in one place and patients in another, he would see that there was so much that all had in common that he could not afford to neglect his sick brothers. He could not, for selfish as well as humane reasons, put them "out of sight and out of mind." He would make sure that his hospitals were not overcrowded, "from which condition other evils arise." He would recognize that a neglected state hospital keeps crying out that mental health is not considered important in his community. To allow a large hospital to be overcrowded, inefficient, and uneconomical is a reflection of poor mental health in all the citizens who live in its vicinity.

A potential danger to the development of good state and private hospitals lies in the promising new drugs and other discoveries of recent years. Hearing about the good effects of the drugs, a legislator begins to think that state hospitals will need no new personnel or buildings. "Wonder drugs" will solve the tremendous problem and lift the burden now on the shoulders of the state. Or boarding-out schemes, which have worked well in Holland, will cut down the number of hospital patients. Treatment along psychoanalytic lines has produced remarkable recoveries. Mental hygiene groups send out posters saying that "85% of the mentally ill can be cured," so why provide more hospital beds? All this can discourage and delay progress.

Now to look at all these new gifts closely. The effects of the new drugs are amazing, but their ability to tranquilize is much greater than their capacity to cure. They deserve intense research in hospitals which are fully equipped with skillful personnel. Boarding out is more difficult in a mixed population such as ours than in homogeneous European countries. Psychoanalytic methods are time-consuming, and again need the hospital personnel who can give individual attention to the patients. That "85% of the mentally ill can be cured" seems optimistic, especially if you consider the increasing number of old-age mental illnesses at one end of our line, and at the other end people who have severe prejudices. The estimate of 85 per cent recovery applies only to one part of our line.

This, certainly, is true. With all these new helps, psychiatric hospitals which have modern buildings and equipment and adequate staffs—now possessed by only 3 out of 83—can do wonders. With trained personnel the newer and older methods can be applied with discrimination to each individual. If so, we can expect so many recoveries that the burden to the state will be gradually lessened.

The good mental hospital, under these definitions, is not a place to put away unhappy, unfortunate, and unwell people, either at the public expense or their own, until they die at last to make room for more. It should be a station of hope where they can be treated by methods appropriate to each individual, and as quickly as possible, so that they can go back to useful living.

Chapter XIX

ONE MIND,
COMMON TO ALL

A CENTRAL IDEA, which I hope has been developed in every chapter of this book, is that there is value in imagining a great line of the men and women of the United States arranged according to the amount of normality that is in them. The value of this idea is not lessened if normality cannot be measured as exactly as can height. There is such a line, no matter what normality may be.

Many years ago I heard a chemist say that only things that could be measured had importance; last year I read somewhere that "nothing that can be measured has much importance." I like this second way of putting it. Suppose that the long line were arranged exactly according to measured height; it would have some slight value as a statistic, but it would lead to little else. Suppose that the line is arranged loosely according to a variable notion of what is normality and we have a powerful idea that leads in many constructive directions.

It is an old idea that there is "one mind common to all." The long line of people whom I have met confirms it in modern and forceful terms. What reading I have done confirms it. And yet it is a notion deeply resented by many men and women who take for granted that their own minds are free from the imperfections of that common mind. In this book I have been trying to make the idea of one mind more acceptable.

For the sake of simplicity I left children out of the line, although it is obvious that the minds of people under twenty-one years of age have many resemblances to the minds of their elders, and vice versa. I also left out the feebleminded, although the likenesses between them and most of us are greater than we think—except for the rather minor matter of intelligence.

This last word compels me to pause. It occurs to me that intelligence has played little part in determining anyone's place in the line of normality. Intelligent people are to be found everywhere, from top to bottom. A bright and unreliable person stands low; a person with a low IQ who is steady, unselfish, and faithful stands high. The sort of intelligence which can be measured is obviously of little importance in determining how normal a person may be.

While I have limited myself to the likenesses found in the United States in terms of normality only, others have been engaged in broader surveys. Anthropologists have come upon the same elementary thoughts and fundamental emotions in the different cultures they have examined. James A. Michener, in *The Voice of Asia*, says that we delude ourselves by insisting that other peoples and races are different—a dangerous delusion. By different we usually mean inferior, and we have nearly lost more than one war by believing that one American is worth two or ten or twenty "foreigners." Two Quaker women, after visiting families in Europe, Israel, Pakistan, India, Thailand, the Philippines, and Japan, said, "You need only to understand their problems to find that people the world over are wonderfully alike, though they live and dress and talk differently."

In recent years a vivid argument for the likeness of all men appeared in the exhibition of photographs called *The Family of Man*, collected under the direction of Edward Steichen and published for The Museum of Modern Art in 1955.* The pictures speak for themselves, but a sentence of Steichen's sums them up. They are: "a mirror of the essential oneness of mankind throughout the world." The prologue by Carl Sandburg says the same thing in many poetic ways; his phrase, "there is

* Simon and Schuster, Inc., New York.

only one man in the world," parallels that of Emerson—"one mind common to all."

To stimulate thinking I turned from the line of people whom I had known to lines of people I had read about in books and periodicals. Because they are in print, these fictional and real characters tend to be more vivid. Not much is written about ordinary folk, but the equally real people we meet in books teach us just by being themselves and by being willing to talk about themselves. The imagined characters are described by poets and writers who give us the benefit of their deep insight. All these people from the printed page fall into a line which resembles our first line closely enough.

And then there is a most sketchy line of "great" people. It is interesting as a psychologist's attempt to measure greatness, despite a universal belief, shared by the psychologist himself, that greatness is another quality that cannot be measured.

The two lines from a bookshelf tend to emphasize the importance of the middle of any line, and it is this rather inconsistent middle which most insistently brings up the question, "What is normal?"

I had hoped to find some answers to this pivotal question in the very process of building the lines, and I believe they do show that normality can be expressed in degree.

A direct attack on normality was the study of college students chosen for positive indications of success, plus the negative indication that they were apparently not in trouble. These students again lined up. At the top they were steady, creative, and spontaneous with very minor faults. At the center came students with as great assets but with flaws of a major sort—retreats, anxieties, hatreds. At the bottom were a group in whom strong and weak forces were near a balance. They were all normal, but some were decidedly "more so." With students it is appropriate to think of normal as a passing mark in all aspects of college life.

Indirectly it was noticed that normal was not synonymous with average, or perfect, or adjusted, or comfortable.

Adjusted and comfortable are words that describe very well the people of socialistic and yet democratic Sweden. In that lovely land you find few of the tensions and enthusiasms and strivings of more heterogeneous and incomplete nations; its people are well provided for. There is not much to worry about in industry, politics, or religion. So now a Swede says, "Life has become rather empty; we have to replace the tensions of the *normal* battle of life by artificial fears and by personal tensions—by neurosis!" In this peaceful and "most advanced welfare state" the suicide rate is high.*

The best we can do is not to define and limit the meaning of normal but to describe it as a direction and a goal, as freedom from inappropriate bonds, as an ability to decide present-day issues on the basis of present-day emotions and reasoning. To be normal is to possess a flexible, changing ability to focus on main purposes, to "work and love with ease, happiness, and efficiency somewhat in proportion to the circumstances."

These ideas about the normal were made more definite by bringing in the notion of emotional maturity, which has some useful and easily understood aspects. And the discussion of what it means to grow up raised three important questions. What are the inner forces which make people willing to take on new burdens of responsibility each year? What inner forces persuade them to give up the unending struggle? What conflicts of principle, especially relating to conscience, help or hinder growth?

The great inner force that pushes people up on our line is the principle of growth. We like to grow with other people of our own ages, to keep up with them. The assumption of responsibility has rewards as well as burdens. There is something in a long-term purpose that gives a wonderful feeling of security. The hard way for the moment is the easy way in the long run.

The great inner force that tends to pull us down is the principle of ease. It is "anything to keep the baby quiet" for the

* Paul Anderson, "Sweden—The Egalitarian Paradise," *The Listener*, May 31, 1956.

moment; anything to avoid the obstacle ahead; anything to forget some fear, some coming test, some promotion with more
responsibility, some change in familiar habits. "To sleep, to
dream, to drift, to postpone—what attractiveness is here!"

The vital answer to the third question is that the two principles of growth and ease need not be antagonistic. The principle of ease can be made to help growth; a man can work and
sleep and rest for a distant goal. Difficulty arises only when ease
is used to avoid work or trouble. In conscience the principles of
perfection and compromise can collide or work together. One
person's "conscience" may be negative, diseased, perverted,
cruel, distorted, defective, blind, murderous; this is really a
pseudo-conscience. A true inner conscience will be positive, affirmative, clear, and fully mature—a mark of the normal, constructive, and living man or woman.

Looking back over these immense and ancient inner forces,
it is evident that most of the climbing and sliding on the line is
done without benefit of psychiatrists. These physicians are of
some direct help when they cure neurotic or psychotic illness.
They help indirectly when they develop the art of listening,
apply to a patient's problem some inner information on prejudice, and make suggestions to the family doctor.

A special concern of psychiatrists and research workers in the
basic sciences has been the effect of listening to oneself without
distractions. Its power has been demonstrated, and some reasons
are shown for the tendency of most people to avoid such an
experience. Apparently we rely on stimuli from outside to keep
our mental balance.

Some of the effects of living without incoming stimuli were
mentioned in the story *Absent in the Spring*, in which a woman
could look only at sand dunes, and in the real experience of
Anne Morrow Lindbergh, who watched in solitude the sand
dunes and the sea. But the last astounding word on the subject
comes from Dr. John Lilly, of the National Institute of Mental
Health, who arranged to float volunteers in a tank of water at

body temperature in a soundproof chamber with no one else
in the room. The subjects wore only a diver's mask for air in-
take and could see only the bottom of the tank. Soon all the
subjects' minds turned in on themselves; their thinking became
chaos, and it was time for a rescue.

Most of us, following the example of some mental patients
who carry activity to an extreme, manage to keep so busy, so
distracted by every new stimulus from talking, playing, reading,
receiving radio and television programs, that we protect ourselves from both the value and the danger of self-communion.
Please recall the exhilarated woman who in horror looked down
at the floor for one moment of self-realization. In order not to
take that downward look we can drink ourselves toward oblivion
or find in action a means of shutting out any still, small voice.

It is reassuring, despite these extreme examples, to know that
in fifteen minutes a day of self-communion there is power without danger.

In the deep recesses of the laboratories of psychiatric research
Dr. John Lilly has brought about immense changes in animals'
moods and behavior by applying electrical stimuli directly to
the brain. His experiments raise the question of what other
agents might produce the same or similar effects on human
beings. And this has meaning for everyone. The power of a
drug to push one very sick mental patient far up on the line
arouses hopes—and some misgivings—about the possible drug
treatments and effects of the future.

An example is that of a social worker who became mentally
ill in a peculiar (katatonic) way. She did not speak, and every
muscle in her body seemed to be stiff and awkward; her face
was a mask. After this condition had continued for a year, with
other symptoms, the patient was given large doses of amobar-
bital (Amytal) for about a week, whereby she was kept asleep
and aroused only for feeding and bedpan. As she came out of
sleepiness she was a different person, lively and talking with

animated facial expression, easy and graceful in her body movements. After three days, as the effects of the drug wore off, she
returned to her symptoms and at the end of a week was as stiff
in body and unapproachable in mind as ever.

The power in this old-fashioned drug helps us to understand
the effects of the new tranquilizers which can be used over
longer periods of time. Already they have had a good effect on
sick people, especially those in mental hospitals. Already they
have been of some use in "quieting nerves." But might they
some day be used for a community to bring calmness, to abolish
anxiety, to make people conform? It is not difficult to imagine
the dictators of Russia sending carloads of tranquilizers to
Poland, Hungary, and Rumania, and perhaps to all university
students.

A lot of unpleasant things are suggested in these alliterative
words—calmness, contentment, comfort, corruption. They in
turn suggest their opposite, a "divine discontent." A satisfied
person is hopeless; men and women, with all their resemblances,
are better off to keep those endearing, interesting, unreasoning
little differences and anxieties that make each of them an individual in his own right. Deliver us from easy contentment, from
uniformity and someone else's ideas of perfection! Over and
over let us admit that a little neurosis is needed for mental
health.

It is time to take a final look at the three imperfectly separated
parts of the line.

The upper part has in it as examples Virgil and Dante, guide
and follower, both brilliant, and George Washington and a
mother-in-law, not so brilliant. In all four there stands out
steadiness of purpose, loyalty, reliability, and acceptance of
responsibility. On the solid foundation of very normal people
such as these our society is built.

The lessons they all teach are plain. But we hope for the
thousands now at the top of our line a willingness to learn

from those below them. We hope they may find that wonderful things can come from disorderly minds; we hope they may see that other peoples' failures are their own weaknesses.

It is in the mid-part of our line that we find great gifts and great faults. The very presence of a talent tends to make a person lopsided. A boy who has musical genius cannot be allowed to play baseball and perhaps damage a finger; he is set aside from other boys; he cannot develop exactly as the others do. He is predisposed both to greatness and to trouble.

Suppose a man has a genius for painting and wants to do nothing but paint. If people do not buy his pictures during his lifetime he starves; he may begin to hate the well-ordered, conventional people above him on the line and perhaps become disorderly, drunken, or more reckless. But it must be remembered that neither eccentricities or disorders *make* a man a genius, and that a society composed entirely of geniuses would not endure for one day. The middle of the long line needs the two ends.

There remains the third part of the line, composed of human beings who are temporarily or for a long time deprived of the controlling parts of their minds. Here I must repeat what I have said before. When I say that some of them are carried away by their emotions and are unreasonable, that others are caught up in daydreams or are continually blaming other people for their own faults, whom am I describing? There but for the grace of God go all of us. Again I repeat that the men and women in this third section have illnesses which split them and let us look inside them, or illnesses that simply exaggerate traits which usually escape notice or which most people have in embryo. They give us insight into our deeper selves; they are our contemporary ancestors, less civilized, less sophisticated, more truthful than we. What is learned from them can be applied to any part of our line.

On his ninetieth birthday George Bernard Shaw in a newspaper interview said that he was unconcerned whether he had "come into this world mad—or a little too sane—which is the same thing."

Some day a daring person might try to line up the men and women of the United States in terms of *good* instead of *normal*, with saints above and sinners below. Such a person probably would have difficulty in finding totally good or totally evil people, but he would have no trouble in locating some that were 90 per cent or 10 per cent good. Toward the middle of the line he would come upon the same kinds of puzzles that beset the mid-normal. He would find dirty saints and clean sinners, irritable and uncomfortable saints and pleasant sinners. One man's unselfishness might be another's pride. In some cases he would find holiness and sin waging an even battle; in others there would be a contented compromise.

Comments from my favorite book, *The Way of All Flesh*, fi, in here. "The devil . . . when he dresses in angel's clothes can only be detected by experts of exceptional skill, and so often does he adopt this disguise that it is hardly safe to be seen talking to an angel at all. . . . Rare virtues are like rare plants or animals, things that have not been able to hold their own in the world. A virtue to be serviceable must . . . be alloyed with some commoner but more durable metal." *

Standing out above all confusion and doubt about the exact degrees of the normal or the good is the power of love—the sort of love which favors growth, which meets changes gladly, which sets people free, which does not absorb or dominate, which has no interest in holding back the clock. In many families the clock is stopped, but time has a way of going forward without it. Love moves, grows, says "yes" to time and life.

I hope that readers of this book will build a line of imperfect human beings for themselves, placing themselves and others where they think they belong. They will find it reassuring to see how far down the line there is normal thinking and acting.

* From Samuel Butler, *The Way of All Flesh*. The Macmillan Company, New York, 1925, pages 90 and 92.

It is useful to see that what helps one human being helps all. It is a matter of pride to see the overwhelming majority of individuals in the United States acting in a fully normal, mature way, as when they accept the results of a national election. It is valuable to see that all individuals have the same downward and upward pulls in different degree, and also to see that every individual has to climb to stay in the same place. It is stimulating to realize that the hard ways are best in the long run.

This book begins and ends, then, on the same thesis: "There is one mind common to all individual men. Every man is an inlet to the same, and to all of the same."

We have partly normal minds and we are all imperfect—a reassuring and challenging situation. With a little more willingness to learn from all sorts of people and apply what we learn to ourselves, we can all climb one notch in the scale, perhaps more. In our hates, animosities, and prejudices, as well as our loves, we are so much alike.